BArricades
Across *the*

OXFORD*Playscripts*

• •

Series Editor – Bill Lucas

Joan Lingard   *adapted by David Ian Neville*

Across *the* Barricades

Oxford University Press

Oxford University Press, Walton Street, Oxford OX2 6DP

Oxford   New York
Athens   Auckland   Bangkok   Bombay
Calcutta   Cape Town   Dar es Salaam   Delhi
Florence   Hong Kong   Istanbul   Karachi
Kuala Lumpur   Madras   Madrid   Melbourne
Mexico City   Nairobi   Paris   Singapore
Taipei   Tokyo   Toronto

and associated companies in
Berlin   Ibadan

Oxford is a trade mark of Oxford University Press

Original novel **Across the Barricades** © Joan Lingard,
published by Hamish Hamilton, 1972.
This adaptation © David Ian Neville, published by
Oxford University Press, 1990.
Reprinted 1991 (twice), 1992, 1993, 1994, 1995
This collection © Oxford University Press, 1990.
Activities in this collection © Bill Lucas.

All enquiries concerning professional or amateur
performing rights for this adaptation of **Across the
Barricades** should be addressed to David Ian Neville,
c/o Oxford University Press, Walton Street, Oxford
OX2 6DP.

ISBN 0 19 831272 5

Typeset by Times Graphics

Printed and bound in Great Britain at the University Press, Cambridge

Thanks to Ian Brown, Maggie Kinloch, Eve Jamieson and the
cast of Tag Theatre Company's production of **Across the
Barricades.**

A CIP catalogue record for this book is available from the
British Library.

Contents

Introduction: Ireland today

Kevin

I'd like to walk down a street where there were no soldiers with guns, no policemen with their fingers on triggers ... and no graffiti on the walls ... there must be more to life than all of that.

Many people are troubled because of the violence of life in Northern Ireland. This map, and the explanation which follows it, may help you to understand the problems which prevent peace in Northern Ireland.

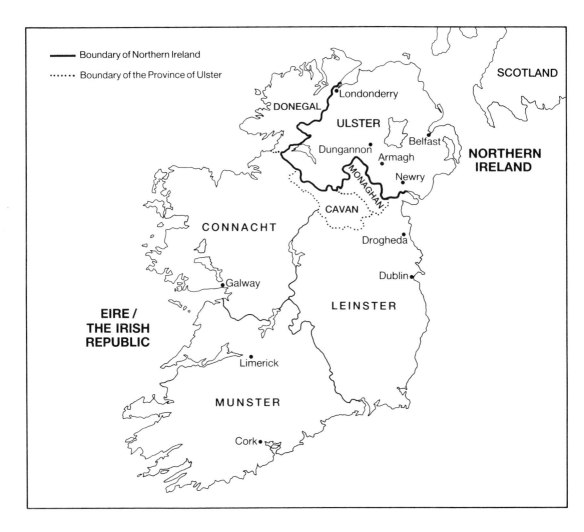

Boundary of Northern Ireland

Boundary of the Province of Ulster

SCOTLAND

Londonderry

DONEGAL

ULSTER

Dungannon

Belfast

NORTHERN IRELAND

Armagh

Newry

MONAGHAN

CAVAN

CONNACHT

Drogheda

Galway

Dublin

LEINSTER

EIRE / THE IRISH REPUBLIC

Limerick

MUNSTER

Cork

Ireland today is divided into two parts.

The South is an independent country called Eire or the Irish Republic. It has its own government and parliament in Dublin. It is made up of three provinces: Connacht, Leinster and Munster. It also contains a small part of Ulster.

The North is part of the United Kingdom. It is ruled by Parliament in London and has the Queen as its head of state.

The violence in **Across the Barricades** has many complicated causes. It centres on the question of whether the North should remain part of the United Kingdom or whether it should join the Irish Republic in some way.

Northern Ireland,
Voting patterns in
the 1987 General Election

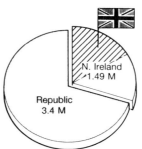

All Ireland population,
1981 = 4.89 million

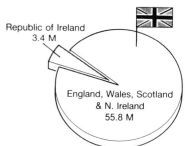

The British Isles,
1981 population = 59.2 million

Unionist population

This question has resulted in conflict for three main reasons:

1 **The people of the North cannot agree about the answer.**
One side want to stay part of the UK. They are called Unionists or
Loyalists. They are mostly Protestants.
The other side want the North to join the South and become part of
the Irish Republic. They are called Nationalists or Republicans. They
are mostly Catholics.

2 **Both sides have private armies willing to use the bullet rather than the
ballot to solve the problem.**
Although most Irish people do not support the use of violence, these
private armies are preventing a peaceful solution to the conflict.

3 **The governments of the UK and the Irish Republic cannot agree about
their answers.**
Their exact attitude varies from time to time, depending on the political
party in power but since 1969 each has stuck to the same general line.
The British government has said that it will not withdraw from
Northern Ireland unless or until a majority of the people there agree to
this.
Look at the graphs.

• Which side is in the majority in Northern Ireland: Unionists or
Nationalists?

• Which side would be in a majority in the whole of Ireland?

• Who ought to have a say in the decision about the future of
Northern Ireland?

Across the Barricades is set in Belfast.

The play was first performed by Tag Theatre Company in 1986 on tour
in Scotland.

Characters

• • • • • • • • • • • • • • • •

Sadie Jackson   *Sadie is a sixteen-and-a-half year old Protestant living in Belfast. At the start of the play she is working in a department store in the centre of Belfast. She is energetic, good humoured and has a determined and stubborn streak in her character.*

Kevin McCoy   *Kevin is seventeen, Catholic and lives a few streets away from Sadie. He works in Dan Kelly's scrapyard. He is hard working and easy going, but like Sadie he is also stubborn. Both Kevin and Sadie have decided not to follow the 'crowd' and neither is easily led.*

Brede McCoy   *Brede is Kevin's younger sister. When they were younger Kevin and his friends were involved in street fights with the Protestant kids who lived nearby, but Brede would never get involved. She was 'the only peace loving one amongst them'. On one occasion, while innocently watching a street fight, she got badly injured and nearly died.*

Tommy Jackson   *Tommy is Sadie's brother. He works in the shipyards like his father. But unlike his father he refuses to join the Orange Lodge. After taking part in the street fight in which Brede McCoy nearly died, Tommy has refused to march on the Twelfth of July. For a time when he was younger Tommy and Sadie became friends with Kevin and Brede. But after a while they grew apart because it was too difficult for them to see each other.*

Mr Jackson   *Sadie's father*

Mrs Jackson   *Sadie's mother*

Uncle Albert   *Kevin's uncle. Albert is Kevin's father's brother. Albert is one of life's optimists. Despite the Troubles and the fact that he never has a proper job and that his old car never works properly, he can always manage a smile and a joke.*

Brian Rafferty   *Brian has been a friend of Kevin's since they were both kids. But now they are growing apart. Some say that Brian is getting mixed up with the Provisional IRA.*

Kate Kelly   *Kate is Brede's friend. Kate is keen on Kevin and they are friends, but they are not going out with each other, at least that's how Kevin sees it.*

Linda Mullet   *Linda lives next door to Sadie and they have been friends for years, but now Sadie has little time for Linda.*

Mrs Mullet   *Linda's mum is a 'good' neighbour to Mrs Jackson – good at borrowing things, good at keeping up with all the local gossip and good at blaming Sadie for being a bad influence on Linda.*

Mr Mullet   *Linda's dad and a friend of Mr Jackson.*

Mr Blake   *Mr Blake is a retired schoolteacher who used to teach at Sadie's school. He lives in the quiet suburbs of Belfast.*

Steve   *A friend of Linda Mullet's*

Newsreader

Teenager 1

Teenager 2

Soldier 1

Soldier 2

Neighbours in Sadie's street/crowd

The play
....

The scenes take place in various parts of Belfast and in Sadie and Kevin's homes. The first impression of the set should be of either a wasteland or junk yard filled with assorted objects including an old armchair, a table, old tyres, old boxes etc. Throughout the play these objects can be used as props for the various scenes. Among the junk there is a broken or twisted barrier which gives the impression of dividing the acting area. It need not be in the middle, or divide the acting area in two equal sections, it can be moved around throughout the play, but is a constant element of division both physically and symbolically.

During the play 'key' areas of the acting area will represent 'Sadie's home and street' and 'Kevin's home and street'. The play can be performed with an audience on three sides of the acting area. The back wall of the acting area can be used for entrances and exits, but performers can also enter through the audience.

....

Scene 1

We hear opening music, [then we see a number of slides of children in Northern Ireland*]. **Sadie** enters and sits on the ground down stage right. She begins looking through a bundle of old photographs... We hear her and **Kevin's** voices on tape, as if being interviewed on the radio...

* Note: When the play was first performed by Tag Theatre Company touring schools it was decided not to use slide projection – stage directions referring to the use of slides have been left in the script as an option. In the original production specially commissioned music was used effectively throughout as indicated.

Sadie	*(Voice-over)* We were kids then . . . I was about thirteen, Kevin was . . . how old were you?
Kevin	*(Voice-over)* Fourteen . . . *(Clears his throat)*
Sadie	Everyone round my bit was getting ready for the Twelfth Day of July* . . . Tommy, that's my brother, he was practising the flute . . .
Kevin	*(Laughs)* And you were going to be a majorette!
Sadie	Don't laugh, I was serious about it then . . . anyway the first time I met Kevin, he'd come round to our street and . . . well, him and this guy, Brian, started painting over our mural of King Billy.**
Kevin	We made a right mess of it . . .
Sadie	Anyway we caught them red-handed and ran after them . . .
Kevin	Brian got away, but I tripped over my shoe-lace . . .
Sadie	He always says that . . . it's rubbish, I pushed you to the ground . . .
Kevin	Oh yeh!
Sadie	Well anyway that was the first time we actually spoke . . . we wanted to beat each other up . . .
Kevin	But being the kind generous sort of person I am, I let her go . . .
Sadie	You mean I let you go . . .
Kevin	Rubbish!
Sadie	Well, the point is, for a while after we were sworn enemies . . . Tommy and I went into the Catholic area to get our own back . . . and it just went on and on from there . . .

* The Twelfth of July was the date of the Battle of the Boyne in 1690, when the Protestant William of Orange defeated the Catholic armies of James II. Protestants celebrate this day with marching bands and banners.
** 'King Billy' is the nickname for King William of Orange.

Kevin	Brian and I went back into the Protestant area . . . it was just a game . . . they made a move, we made a move . . .
Sadie	But all that was years ago . . . a lot of water's passed under the bridge since then as they say . . .

We hear a 'sting' of music, like you would hear on local radio before the news bulletin, then we hear the following news report . . .

Newsreader	Loyalists have claimed responsibility for a petrol bomb attack on a Falls Road pub and the Provisional IRA have said they were behind the explosion which destroyed a supermarket in the Shankhill Road. Weather in the Province will remain warm this evening, with sunny spells tomorrow throughout the day. Not too many problems reported on the roads at the moment, rush hour traffic in Belfast is flowing smoothly . . . *(fade)*

*During the report **Sadie** has put the photographs away in her bag. She combs her hair and puts on her jacket or coat . . . She's leaving work . . .*

Sadie	*(To audience)* It had just been a normal day, I'd been bored stiff working in the hat department, watching all these stupid women try on some really awful hats . . . *(Putting on a voice)* Yes madam that's really nice, goes lovely with your outfit – ould stuck up bitches! I was glad to get out at five thirty . . . I'd spent the whole afternoon daydreaming and counting the minutes on the department clock, which is always five minutes slow . . .

***Kevin** appears behind **Sadie**.*

Kevin	*(Calls)* Sadie? . . . Sadie Jackson?
Sadie	*(To audience)* I was on my way to the bus stop, and all of a sudden I hear this fella shouting my name . . . Oh I recognised him all right . . . it's just it was a bit of a shock, know what I mean?
Kevin	Sadie? I thought it was you.
Sadie	Kevin! . . . *(laughs)* Kevin McCoy!

Kevin	Well, well, haven't seen you in ages . . .
Sadie	Years more like . . . must be about three . . .
Kevin	At least. So what you doing with yourself these days?
Sadie	You really want to know?
Kevin	Sure.
Sadie	I'm eh . . . training to be a brain surgeon.
Kevin	*(Laughs)* Oh, of course, I should have guessed!
Sadie	What about you?
Kevin	Oh . . . em . . . the same, you know . . . *(They laugh)* You fancy a cup of coffee? Have you time?
Sadie	Don't see why not.
Kevin	I know a brillant little place round the corner does wonderful cappuccino . . .
Sadie	Oh get you . . . first of all it was coffee, now it's cappuccino!
Kevin	Well us brain surgeons we do have sophisticated tastes.
Sadie	*(To audience)* I could have said hello and goodbye and left it at that. It would have been easier, less trouble. But life's never that simple, is it?
Kevin	*(To audience)* Sadie was even better looking than I thought she'd be. Like, I remember when we were kids I thought she might turn into an all-in wrestler, she wouldn't let butter melt in her mouth, I'm telling you . . .

*Sadie's friend, **Linda Mullet**, appears . . .*

Linda	Hi, Sadie, you going for the bus?
Sadie	Oh, hi Linda . . .

Linda	Well, well, who's this you're with? Don't I get an introduction? . . . Wait a minute. I've seen you before, haven't I?
Sadie	*(Sourly)* Everyone's seen him before.
Linda	No, I know the face . . .
Kevin	Yeh? I've had it for a while.
Linda	I remember you . . . You're Kevin McCoy and you live up the Falls.
Kevin	Well done, you've won the star prize!
Linda	I knew I'd seen you before.
Sadie	Well, I'm glad you won't have to sit worrying about it all the way home on the bus.
Linda	Haven't seen you for a while . . .
Kevin	You obviously don't frequent the right places, do you?
Linda	I'm not sure I'd want to. Well, Sadie, are you coming for the bus?
Sadie	Not right now, Linda, I'm staying in town.
Linda	Oh are you then? *(She looks at Kevin)* Oh well, in that case I'll leave you to it. Be seeing you, Sadie.
Sadie	No doubt.

Linda walks off.

Kevin	She can't get home quick enough to spread the news.
Sadie	Let her spread what she likes.
Kevin	I was thinking . . . eh . . . if you're not in a rush, maybe we could go for a walk somewhere.
Sadie	It's a nice evening, we could take a walk up Cave Hill.

| Kevin | Good idea. |

They go off.

• •

Scene 2

Sadie's house, evening. **Mrs Jackson,** *Sadie's mother, is setting the table and preparing the evening meal.* **Mr Jackson** *comes in and sits on the armchair reading the evening paper.*

| Mrs Jackson | Are you going to the Lodge* tonight, Jim? |

| Mr Jackson | I always go to the Lodge on a Tuesday. |

| Mrs Jackson | Just asking, that's all. |

Tommy comes in.

| Tommy | Is tea ready yet, Ma? I'm starvin'. |

| Mr Jackson | You should be asking him if he's going to the Lodge. |

| Tommy | Aw, Dad, we've been through all that and I've told you it's not for me. |

| Mr Jackson | Huh! |

| Tommy | Are we ready to eat? I'm meant to be going out. |

| Mrs Jackson | Oh it's ready all right. I'm just wondering where that sister of yours has got to. You'd think I had nothing to do but stand here slaving over a hot stove for her convenience. She's got no consideration for other people. |

| Tommy | Sadie would give you her last penny if you needed it. |

| Mrs Jackson | If she had one to give. Her pay packet's spent before she gets it. |

* The Lodge is a meeting place for members of the Orange Order, a society set up by Protestants in the 1790s.

Mr Jackson	Come on, Aggie, let's eat. I've to be at the Lodge for seven.
	*From offstage we hear someone knocking at the door. It's **Linda**...*
Linda	*(offstage)* Anybody in?
	***Linda** enters. **Mr Jackson** is obviously annoyed that his meal is going to be delayed even more.*
Mr Jackson	Hello, Linda, did you get fed up waiting on Tommy?
Linda	Hello... oh sorry, I didn't realise you'd still be eating.
Mrs Jackson	We're a bit later tonight. You haven't seen Sadie in your travels, have you?
Linda	Well I did actually. I saw her on my way home, but I don't think she was on her way home.
Mrs Jackson	So where was she going? She might have told us.
Linda	I don't know where she was going, but ...
Mrs Jackson	But what?
Linda	Oh nothing.
Tommy	I'll be ready in a few minutes, Linda, I was thinking we could go to the cinema...
Mrs Jackson	What were you going to say, Linda?
Linda	*(Hesitantly)* Well... Sadie wasn't alone.
Mr Jackson	Oh. And who was she with?
Linda	I don't know if I should tell you that.
Tommy	Maybe you shouldn't then. I'm not feeling that hungry, come on, Linda, let's get on our way.

Mrs Jackson	Just a minute, Tommy.
Mr Jackson	I think Linda knows something we ought to know.
Linda	I don't want to cause any trouble . . .
Mrs Jackson	If there's something you think we ought to know you must tell us.
Tommy	Let's go, Linda.
Mr Jackson	Well, Linda, what have you got to say for yourself?

> *Linda looks nervously at Tommy, but she can't stop herself from telling them about Kevin.*

Linda	I suppose you've got a right to know . . . she was with that Catholic boy, Kevin McCoy.
Mrs Jackson	What are you talking about, Linda?
Linda	It was that boy Sadie and Tommy got mixed up with three summers ago, the one whose sister got hurt. They were waiting on a bus together.
Mr Jackson	What do you know about this, Tommy?
Tommy	Nothing. I don't see what the fuss is all about, I mean it's not as if she's going to marry him.
Mrs Jackson	Marry him? Oh no . . .
Tommy	She hasn't seen him in years, Mum, there's nothing in it!

> *Pause.* **Mrs Jackson** *is in a state of shock.* **Mr Jackson** *is comforting her.* **Linda** *is trying to avoid looking at Tommy.* **Tommy** *stares at her.*

Tommy	I'm going to the pictures. You can come if you want.

> ***Tommy*** *walks out without waiting for a reaction from Linda.* ***Linda*** *looks uneasily at Mr and Mrs Jackson and then follows Tommy out.* ***Mrs Jackson*** *begins clearing the table, her hands shaking. She is almost frantic.* ***Mr Jackson*** *follows her off stage.*

. . . .

Scene 3

Cave Hill, evening. ***Sadie*** *and* ***Kevin*** *enter and sit downstage.*

Sadie	It's beautiful up here, isn't it?
Kevin	I love Cave Hill. I like sitting here, looking down on the city.
Sadie	It looks so peaceful.
Kevin	It does you good to get out of the city of an evening.
Sadie	There's no one to bother you up here . . .
Kevin	Does it worry you about Linda seeing us?
Sadie	It's none of her business.
Kevin	Thought she was your best friend?
Sadie	You're joking. Linda Mullet? She's just like her father, always out to cause trouble . . . Don't know what our Tommy sees in her . . .
Kevin	So Tommy's going around with Linda?
Sadie	She drags him all over Belfast and he pays.
Kevin	Has he got a job then?
Sadie	He works down there in the shipyards. What about you, have you got a job?

Kevin   Aye, remember Kate Kelly, you know, Brede's friend?

Sadie   Yeh, what about her?

Kevin   I'm working in her father's scrapyard.

Sadie   Really? And does she go with the job?

Kevin   Very funny!

Sadie   She used to fancy you rotten, didn't she?

Kevin   Hm, and what about you? What you up to these days?

Sadie   Trying to change the subject are we? *(Laughs)* Must be some life roaming the streets looking for scrap.

Kevin   Well some of the scrap isn't exactly what we're looking for . . .

Sadie   What about all these burnt out cars and things?

Kevin   You daren't touch them, people use them . . . Burnt out cars, buses, torn-up paving stones, barbed wire, it might be scrap to you and me, but it comes in handy for building barricades . . . oh it's fun roaming the streets of Belfast, you see a bit of life . . .

Sadie   Ah well, let's forget about all that.

Kevin   Yeh, you're right.

                                   Pause as they look around taking in the view.

Sadie   It's funny seeing you after all this time.

Kevin   And you . . .

Sadie   I mean after all, we only stay a few streets away from each other . . .

Kevin   Yeh, but it might as well be a thousand miles.

Sadie	Remember when we first met, when we were kids, we were sworn enemies ...
Kevin	It was a good laugh to begin with, a bit of a game right enough ... Kevin's gang, Sadie's gang ... calling each other names ... *(Shouts)* Down with the Prods!
Sadie	*(Shouts)* Down with the Micks!

As they begin to remember the past it comes alive almost like a dream sequence.

Kevin	I remember Brian and me sneaking into the Proddies' area in the middle of the night to paint over your lot's King Billy ...
Sadie	What about when I got into your house in the middle of the night and wrote 'Down with the Pope' on the kitchen table ... it took poor Brede ages to scrape it off ...
Kevin	*(Almost to himself)* Oh it started as a bit of fun all right ...
Sadie	*(Also almost to herself as if remembering a bad dream)* But it ended in a pitched battle ... I remember it as if it was yesterday ... the eleventh of July ... Bonfire Night ... we were on one side of the road, they were on the other ...

Music, sounds of the battle in full flight, children shouting, bin lids being bashed together, stone-throwing ...

Kevin	We'd been building up to it for days ...
Sadie	We started shouting ... 'Down with the Micks! Down with the Pope!'
Kevin	*(Shouts)* Down with King Billy and all the Prods!

At this point other members of the cast appear playing the parts of other kids in the 'battle'. Kevin, Sadie and the others all mime throwing stones and shout 'Down with the Prods' etc. as if the 'battle' is taking place ... During this members of the

*cast and **Sadie** and **Kevin** narrate what happened, their voices charged with the excitement of the battle, almost having to shout above the noise.*

Sadie   People started throwing stones, then bricks . . .

Teenager 1   Anything you could lay your hands on . . .

Teenager 2   People were going mad . . .

Kevin   Everyone was getting carried away with the excitement . . .

Sadie   Everyone except Kevin's sister, Brede . . . she just stood there, not shouting or throwing anything, just watching . . .

*By now **Brede** has appeared in the middle of the battle, but she is not involved, she just stands very still.*

Kevin   Then someone threw a brick, she tried to duck but she wasn't quick enough . . .

Sadie   *(Screams)* Brede!

*Everybody freezes and for a few seconds there is silence, then other members of the cast walk off slowly leaving **Sadie** and **Kevin** alone again.*

Sadie   Brede had never hurt anyone . . . in fact the only time I'd ever met her she'd been very civil to me . . . I ran to help her, it was just something I had to do . . .

| Kevin | *(To Sadie)* I'll never forget that, you and Tommy helping Brede. |

Sadie   All I remember is waiting in that hospital with you, me and Tommy wondering if Brede was going to die. Brede had never harmed a soul and here she was the one that comes out worst when there's trouble . . .

Kevin   After that we became friends. You, me, Tommy, and Brede when she recovered. We had some good times . . . going off to the seaside at Bangor, coming up here, we had a laugh . . .

Sadie   But it all got quite difficult, you know, telling our parents we were going somewhere else . . . so we grew apart and that was that until now . . .

Kevin   *(To Sadie)* We must do it again sometime . . .

Sadie   What?

Kevin   Go to Bangor for the day, you and me like.

Sadie   Well, when do you want to go?

Kevin   How about Saturday?

Sadie   We'll take a picnic, make a day of it, eh?

Kevin   You're on!

Music. **Sadie** *and* **Kevin** *exit.*

. . . .

Scene 4

Sadie's house, late evening. **Mrs Jackson** *is setting out the table for breakfast,* **Mr Jackson** *comes in, back from the Lodge.*

Mr Jackson   Is she back yet?

Mrs Jackson   She's up in her room.

Mr Jackson   Oh, is she now.

Mrs Jackson	How was the Lodge?
Mr Jackson	Mullet was there. He wanted to know what all this was about.
Mrs Jackson	Did he say anything to anyone?
Mr Jackson	You can't keep a thing like this quiet, it's no use pretending ... that girl, honestly, she'll get us all into trouble.
Mrs Jackson	Jim, what are we going to do?

Sadie comes in.

Mr Jackson	I wish I knew ... well, well, you're home?
Sadie	I'm allowed out amn't I?
Mrs Jackson	The whole street's talking about you, Sadie.
Sadie	Linda Mullet, she's the whole street?
Mrs Jackson	*(Whispers)* The Mullets have got connections ...
Sadie	All I've done is go for a walk with a boy.
Mr Jackson	Well, you're not seeing him again, that's for sure, d'you hear?
Sadie	I'll see him if I want to, it's a free world.
Mr Jackson	*(Grabbing her arm)* Is that what you think? Is it?
Sadie	*(Moving away)* Look, leave me alone ...
Mr Jackson	As long as you're under my roof, you'll do what I tell you.
Sadie	I don't need to stay under your roof. I'm sixteen, nearly seventeen, I can do what I want ...
Mrs Jackson	Sadie, that's enough ...
Mr Jackson	Oh, so we're independent now, are we? She's earning twenty-five quid a week and she's independent ...

Sadie	Well, you wanted me to go on that stupid training scheme, didn't you?
Mr Jackson	Ah well, we'd soon see how far you'd get under your own steam. You've got all the ideas, haven't you? You know everything, don't you? You don't seem to realise that we're a family and what you do affects us all.
Mrs Jackson	Jim . . . calm down . . .
Mr Jackson	Next time you choose to go for a walk, you go for a walk with one of your own kind!
Sadie	*(Going)* I'm going to bed, I've had enough of this!

Sadie walks out.

Mr Jackson	*(Shouts)* Sadie! I haven't finished with you yet . . . get back in here this minute!
Mrs Jackson	Leave her be, Jim. You'll only end up turning her against you.

> *We hear music – rebellious, rock – **Mr** and **Mrs Jackson** go off.*
> *Sadie comes back on . . . She begins looking through some old photographs.*

Sadie	*(To audience)* My parents? . . . Well, I suppose they were all right really . . . I mean my father wasn't violent or anything like that, not like some of the people round our way. But he took the Lodge seriously . . . his father was a good Orangeman, so he had to keep up the tradition. He wanted Tommy to join . . . we were both going to march, you know on the Twelfth . . . but then Brede got hurt and we just couldn't go . . . my parents went crazy, they didn't understand . . . we were just kids, but we were 'letting the side down' . . . my father's forever going on at Tommy to join up . . . he gets a lot of stick in work as well . . . but Tommy's not interested . . . I mean does it make you a good Protestant to march through the streets playing a little flute?

> *Sadie goes off, and as the music fades, **Brian** and **Kevin** come on.*

Scene 5

*Kevin's street, early morning. **Kevin** is busy working in Kelly's Scrapyard. **Brian Rafferty** is trying to talk to him. **Kevin** tries to get on with his work moving different bits of scrap around.*

Brian	All I want to know, Kevin, is one thing, are you a good patriot?
Kevin	Brian, what are you going on about?
Brian	I mean you believe in the cause, don't you?
Kevin	Of course. I'm a republican amn't I?
Brian	*(Softer)* We have to be prepared to fight for what we believe in, don't we? I mean you are ready to fight?
Kevin	I don't see what good it would do, to be honest.
Brian	You can't mean that?
Kevin	Look, d'you mind if we discuss all this later on, if I don't get on with my work, Kelly will have a fit.
Brian	Sure. We don't want to get on the wrong side of old man Kelly or for that matter Kate, no doubt she'll have your coffee ready for you soon . . .
Kevin	Yeh, yeh . . .
Brian	Kate was wondering where you were last night, in fact we all were.
Kevin	Listen, let's get this straight, Brian, Kate and I are just friends, all right?
Brian	Have you told her?
Kevin	Drop it, Brian . . .
Brian	A bit touchy today, must have been a late night?
Kevin	Yeh, as a matter of fact it was. Now if you don't mind . . .

Brian	Sure thing, Kevin, don't let me keep you. We'll have a good old chat later, it's important, very important. Anyway I'd better be going myself . . . things to do, people to see, know what I mean . . . see you, Kevin.
Kevin	See you later.

> *Brian goes off. Kevin continues moving some of the scrap around, then looks at his watch and starts to get ready to leave. His sister, Brede, arrives . . .*

Brede	Hi, Kevin, are you finished for the day?
Kevin	Yes, I'd better get home earlier tonight or Ma'll do her nut.
Brede	Who was she, Kevin? The girl you were out with last night?
Kevin	Me? Out with a girl? Never.
Brede	Look, I wasn't born yesterday, I know you. You were in another world this morning at breakfast.
Kevin	I was tired.
Brede	Oh yeh, come on, Kevin.
Kevin	Not much goes past you, Brede.
Brede	So who was she? You can trust me, I won't say a word to Kate.
Kevin	It's got nothing to do with Kate, we're not sworn to each other . . .
Brede	Well, you know how she feels about you.
Kevin	I've never given her any cause to feel like that. Kate's got a good imagination.
Brede	I know. Come on, Kevin . . . tell me . . . is it someone I know?
Kevin	Someone you used to know . . . a while back.
Brede	Stop playing games, you idiot.

Kevin	*(Pause, then)* She lives on the other side.
Brede	It wouldn't be Sadie Jackson by any chance? *(Pause)* It isn't?
Kevin	It is.
Brede	Are you seeing her again?
Kevin	I'm taking her to Bangor on Saturday. We're going to spend the whole day there, have a picnic . . .
Brede	Kevin, d'you think it's wise seeing her again?
Kevin	Aw Brede . . .
Brede	Look, I like Sadie, she's a nice girl, all right . . . but think about it, Kevin, think about where she lives and where you live . . . should you be getting involved with each other?
Kevin	There's a lot of things nobody should be doing these days. Look I'm going to pop in and see Brian before I go home, tell Ma I'll be back soon.

Kevin walks off.

Brede	Kevin!

Music. **Brede** *holds her position for a few seconds, then exits following Kevin.*

• •

Scene 6

Brian's house, evening. **Kevin** *and* **Brian** *enter together.*

Brian	Kevin, I told you I had something important to talk to you about. Glad you could come round . . .
Kevin	Brian, what are you going on about?
Brian	I've got something to show you . . . *(He closes the 'door', checks the window)* Wait until you see this, Kevin, you won't believe it . . .

Kevin	Don't tell me you've got your hands on a stick of dynamite?
Brian	Oh no, this is much better than dynamite . . .

He pulls an old box out from 'under his bed' or some other hiding place, opens it up and unwraps an old army rifle.

	This is something that is going to come in very useful, very useful indeed . . . *(Unwraps rifle)* Ever seen one of them before?
Kevin	Where did you get that?
Brian	Oh it's pretty old, but it still works . . . it's quite a heavy old thing . . . feel it . . .

Kevin takes the rifle, holds it, then quickly gives it back to Brian, almost as if touching it has soiled his hands.

Brian	Oh, it's powerful all right . . . and there's five rounds of ammunition to go with it . . .
Kevin	You're crazy! You're out of your head, Brian.
Brian	*(Angry)* And how exactly do you work that out?
Kevin	You can't keep that thing here, the Brits could be round searching the neighbourhood any time.
Brian	*(Smiles)* Well, that's just it, Kevin, I was thinking of hiding it somewhere . . . somewhere like Ould Kelly's scrapyard.
Kevin	You've got to be kiddin'. The old man would have a fit.
Brian	He doesn't need to know anything about it. You could find a good place to hide it.
Kevin	I don't want anything to do with guns, Brian. It's madness.

Brian	That's not the way you once talked. There was a time when you were full of fighting to get the six counties back from the English. A united Ireland! Up the rebels! What's happened to all that?
Kevin	I was younger then.
Brian	Some excuse that!
Kevin	There's enough people getting killed. I want nothing to do with it.
Brian	You're a coward, that's your trouble.
Kevin	*(Grabbing Brian)* Take that back!
Brian	Give me one good reason.
Kevin	Brede almost died because of all the trouble, or don't you remember?
Brian	*(Breaking away)* Well she's all right now, isn't she?
Kevin	That's not the point. Look, where did you get that thing from anyway?
Brian	Oh, that's right, I'm sure to tell you.
Kevin	You think I'd split on you? Don't be stupid, Brian.
Brian	Look, you want one Ireland, don't you?
Kevin	*(Points to gun)* Not with that I don't.
Brian	There's no other way. Why don't you join us?
Kevin	I'm not afraid of fighting if I see a need for it, but I'm not for people dying.
Brian	But it's the enemy that'll die.
Kevin	You're not such an eejit as to believe that. If there's bullets flying, your mother or mine could be standing in the road.

Brian	So you won't be one of us?
Kevin	*(Moving away)* It's not a game any more.
Brian	Traitor!
Kevin	Call me what you like, Brian. There's dozens of Catholics who aren't one of you either, and don't you forget that!
Brian	If you let on about this you know what'll happen.
Kevin	Just be careful what you do with that thing, you might end up blowing your own head off.

***Brian** points the gun at **Kevin**.*

Brian	Hold it right there Kevin! *(Laughs)* Scared?
Kevin	I told you, it's not a game any more ...

> *They both stand there very still for a few seconds, **Brian**'s finger is on the trigger ... he clicks the trigger, nothing happens ... he laughs ...*

Brian	That got you going, didn't it?
Kevin	You're pathetic, Rafferty, you're really pathetic!

*Kevin pushes past him and walks off, **Brian** follows.*
We see pictures on the screen of Northern Ireland, soldiers on duty, IRA members with dark glasses and balaclavas at funerals firing rifles into the air ... perhaps ending with a street scene with a body lying dead and men with rifles in the background ... army, RUC, IRA, UDA – it's difficult to tell who they are ...
Or alternatively ...
We hear a 'sting' of music and then the following news bulletin ...

Newsreader   Police and army units are today carrying out a house to house search after one man was shot dead and another two men were seriously injured in an incident outside a bar in West Belfast late last night. In another incident city centre streets were cleared with apparently only minutes to spare before a car bomb caused serious damage to buildings in the area. Police received an anonymous tip off, but as yet no organisation has claimed responsibility for the device. Weather prospects for the weekend look good with clear skies and several hours of sunshine forecast for Saturday . . . *(Fade)*

Scene 7

Bangor, Saturday. The sound of the sea, seagulls, wind . . . **Sadie** *and* **Kevin** *are in the middle of a picnic . . .*

Sadie   It's good to be out of Belfast, right enough . . .

Kevin   I love it here, breathing in the fresh air and letting your thoughts drift out to sea. Ever been in a boat, Sadie?

Sadie   Only one of those rowing boats you rent for half an hour.

Kevin   *(Laughs)* One day I'll take you out in a boat and row you all the way to Scotland. Would you like that?

Sadie   When do you want to go?

Kevin   You would too, wouldn't you?

Sadie   You know me, I'm ready for anything. *(She offers him another sandwich)* Here . . . grab another one . . .

Kevin   Thanks. You've made enough to feed an army.

Sadie   I was up at the crack of dawn making them, couldn't let my Ma see me, could I?

Kevin   Aye well, there's a few in my street would be having a heart attack if they could see me now.

Sadie	Wonder what your friend Brian would think?
Kevin	I don't know and I don't care.
Sadie	What's he up to these days?
Kevin	This and that . . . let's forget about your street and mine.
Sadie	Good idea. Want an apple? I brought two . . .
Kevin	*(Taking apple)* You're very domesticated, aren't you?
Sadie	Not really, I just like my grub.
Kevin	*(Laughs)* Sadie, you've done us proud with this little feast.
Sadie	Well, all the fresh air, it gives you an appetite . . .
Kevin	It's so peaceful here, don't you think? It's like we've got the whole world to ourselves.
Sadie	Wouldn't it be nice if we did?
Kevin	Just you and me and all this.
Sadie	Plus some food.
Kevin	*(Laughs)* Of course.
Sadie	Funny we should get on so well together.
Kevin	Why d'you say that?
Sadie	Well you know what I mean, with so many things against it.
Kevin	Only one. And that doesn't seem to matter.
Sadie	No. Not when it's just the two of us together.
Kevin	Does it bother you when we're not?
Sadie	I don't know . . . I find it odd when I think of you going to things like . . . well, like confession.

Kevin	It's just part of my religion.
Sadie	Would you confess to the priest that you were going with a Protestant girl?
Kevin	There's no law against it. It's not a mortal sin.
Sadie	I hate the word sin. They're always going on about the word sin. Don't you resent the power the priests have over you?
Kevin	They don't have much power.
Sadie	'Course they do.
Kevin	Rubbish. You know nothing about it.
Sadie	And these statues and things, I mean honestly . . . I don't know how you can bring yourself to pray to them.
Kevin	What about your lot? Worshipping a silly old Dutchman dead these three hundred years.*
Sadie	We don't worship him. Never have.
Kevin	*(Standing up)* Ah, for God's sake! King Billy on his white horse. Long live King Billy! Keep the Micks down!
Sadie	If there were more of you than there was of us you'd soon keep us down.
Kevin	So you're afraid, that's what it is!

He laughs and moves away.

Sadie	Rubbish.
Kevin	You're all afraid.

* Kevin is talking about William of Orange, a Protestant King of England.

Sadie	You're no better than the rest of them, Kevin McCoy. I hate you!
	Kevin turns his back on her and stands very still.
Sadie	*(To audience)* At that moment I did hate him . . . I felt miserable, I felt so alone . . . I wondered if my father was right, were all Catholics the same?
Kevin	*(To audience)* I walked away, I kept walking . . . I was furious with Sadie. I couldn't believe she was still talking about Catholics in the same old way . . . It's funny when you have an argument, you just respond automatically, you meet each attack with a counter-attack, you say things you don't always mean, there's no time to think . . . Was Sadie just like all the other Protestants?
Sadie	*(To audience)* It started to rain . . . our picnic was ruined. I just sat there, I couldn't move. I wanted to catch pneumonia and die and make Kevin feel guilty . . .
	*Pause – music – **Sadie** sits all huddled up and looking miserable. After a while **Kevin** walks up behind her, kneels down and puts his arms round her . . . the music fades.*
Kevin	Sadie?
Sadie	Oh, you gave me a fright . . .
Kevin	No better than the rest of them, am I?
Sadie	Kevin, I didn't mean it.
Kevin	It was all pretty silly, I'm sorry.
Sadie	So am I. Thanks for coming back.
Kevin	Did you think I was just going to leave you sitting all alone on the sands? Come on, let's go and find some shelter . . .
	They move and sit on the other side of the acting area . . .

Sadie	There's something really special about Bangor, I don't know what, I just love being here ...
Kevin	It's a sort of escape, isn't it? Just think, we've spent the whole day here with no one to bother us ...
Sadie	It's safe ...
Kevin	It's been a good day right enough ...
Sadie	I don't want to go home.
Kevin	Neither do I, but I think we'd better get on our way, it's after half past ten.
Sadie	*(Jumping to her feet)* Oh, Kevin! Come on, we'd better run for it.

> *They both make a mad dash across the stage, but they arrive too late and watch the last bus move off in the distance.*

Sadie	*(Worried)* Ah Kevin, I told you we'd end up missing the last bus ...
Kevin	Not to worry, Sadie. We'll hitch. Someone's bound to give us a lift.
Sadie	At this time of night, are you kidding?
Kevin	There's nothing to worry about, just stick out your thumb and hope for the best!

> ***Sadie*** *thinks about it for a few seconds, and then with a smile on her face she sticks out her thumb and starts hitching.* ***Kevin*** *smiles ...*

Sadie	How am I doing?
Kevin	You've got the wrist action, it's just a pity there aren't any cars going by!

They both laugh.

Sadie   I think we'll be stuck here all night . . .

Kevin   No, look, there's a car coming . . .

> *They both stick their thumbs out and watch several cars go racing by. This happens a few times . . . gradually it becomes more frustrating. **Kevin** mouths obscenities at the speeding cars, **Sadie** laughs . . .*

Kevin   *(Calling after a car)* I hope all your wheels fall off . . .

Sadie   *(Sarcastic)* Not to worry, Kevin, we'll get a lift . . .

Kevin   *(To audience)* And we did . . . suddenly this old banger stopped, it was like an answer to a prayer . . . But my ecstasy did not last long, I recognised the driver . . .

> *By now Kevin's uncle **Albert** has appeared and begins ushering them into his 'car'. The 'car' is made out of old seats that are part of the set. **Uncle Albert** is wearing an old coat and hat and looks like he has a permanent supply of Guinness . . . He is an eternal optimist and good humoured.*

Albert   Well, well, this is an unexpected pleasure. Jump aboard, my boy, you and the young lady, make yourself comfortable!

Kevin   Sadie, this is my Uncle Albert . . .

Sadie   Oh, hello.

Kevin   Uncle Albert meet Sadie.

Albert   Oh, you've been keeping her well hidden, Kevin. *(Laughs)* Oh, you're a right lad and no mistake!

Kevin   *(To audience)* It was embarrassing enough being caught with a girl, but a Protestant? I was sure he was going to catch us out any minute . . .

Albert	That's the stuff, now you can just sit there in the back and have a wee cuddle! I promise not to look!
Kevin	Just keep your eyes on the road, Uncle Albert.
Albert	Why? Does it do tricks? *(Roars with laughter)* Now you two might be wondering what I'm doing out here at this time of night. Well to be honest I went to see a man about a dog! I'm telling the God's honest truth here . . . it was the nicest greyhound I've seen in a long time, beautiful beast . . . Oh I was tempted, but the missus would throw me out if I brought it back home . . .
Sadie	*(To audience)* I liked Kevin's uncle, he was a good laugh, but I was dreading him asking me too much about myself . . .
Albert	So where do you live then, Sadie?
Sadie	*(Off guard)* Em . . . eh . . . not far from Kevin.
Albert	Funny I've never seen you before. I'd have remembered . . . Oh you know how to pick them, Kevin!
Kevin	Don't listen to him, Sadie, he's full of smooth talk.
Sadie	Well, now I know where you get it from.
Albert	*(Laughing, and turning round)* Oh that's a good one! Ah that's what I like . . . she's more than a match for you Kevin!
Kevin	Keep your eyes on the road Uncle.
	Albert *swerves violently, narrowly missing another car.*
Albert	*(Shouts at other driver)* Hey you! Can you not watch where you're going! You eejit! *(Changing his tone)* You must bring Sadie round to meet the wife sometime . . .
	Sadie *and* ***Kevin*** *exchange glances and laugh.*
Sadie	*(Whispers to* ***Kevin****)* This is going to be a very eventful journey, I can tell . . . *(To* ***Albert****)* How far are we from Belfast, Mr McCoy?

Albert	Oh about five miles, not far to go now.
Kevin	Uncle Albert, I don't like to worry you but there's steam pouring out of the engine ...
Albert	*(Albert brakes hard)* Oh no, this is all I need and me with guests aboard! All right, everyone out!

> *They all get out and **Albert** 'opens the bonnet of the car' (mimed). **Albert** starts trying to wave the smoke away, **Kevin** looks in the engine to see what the problem is.*

Albert	Oh my poor little car's taken a nasty turn! Kevin, what am I going to do?
Kevin	It looks like the thermostat has gone. You won't get it fixed at this time of night. We'll need to leave it and walk home ...
Albert	Leave it? Mercy me, they'll have the wheels off it before dawn ... Oh well, I'll just need to get someone out to fix it tomorrow. Honestly, Sadie, it's the first time my wee car's let me down like this ...
Kevin	*(Laughs)* Don't believe a word of it, Sadie.
Albert	Ah well, it won't take us long to get to Belfast, anyway, we'll have a wee song to help us on our way ...

> *They link arms and start walking ... **Albert** starts singing and they join in ...*

Sadie	Oh that's a good idea ...
Albert	*(Starts singing)* Oh Danny Boy, the pipes are calling ... From glen to glen and down the mountain side ...

> ***Albert** changes mid-song to 'The Soldier's Song'. **Kevin** and **Sadie** join in, **Sadie** almost before she realises what she's singing.*

Sadie	*(To audience)* I couldn't believe it, to my own amazement I was joining in singing rebel songs . . . my father would have had heart failure if he'd heard me . . . But we soon stopped singing . . .
Kevin	*(To audience)* We were stopped and questioned by some British soldiers. An army patrol car had been blown up . . . the driver was killed . . .
Sadie	I feel sick, why do people do these things?
Albert	Oh it's terrible right enough, but if they will come over here they have to expect trouble.
Sadie	But the reason they're over here is . . .
Kevin	Sadie!
Albert	Don't get me wrong, Sadie, I'm not for people getting killed, some of these soldiers are just boys . . . I don't know why we can't get a little bit of peace. Oh here's me talking of peace and if I'm not home in a few minutes my missus will be starting World War Three! *(Laughs)* No doubt Kevin'll want you to himself from here on . . .
Kevin	Goodnight, Uncle Albert.
Sadie	Goodnight.
Albert	*(Going)* See you soon I hope, eh Sadie? You get him to bring you round for tea! Night then! *(He goes off)*
Sadie	He's all right, your Uncle Albert, isn't he?
Kevin	Oh he's a good natured soul, but a terrible husband!
Sadie	*(Smiles)* Kevin, I think you should leave me here, I'll make my own way home . . .
Kevin	Aw don't worry, I'll walk you to the end of your street . . .
Sadie	I do worry.
Kevin	It's been a lovely day, Sadie.

Sadie	Well we must do it again and again . . .
Kevin	And again . . .

> *They stand holding hands and looking into each other's eyes. They are about to kiss when **Mr Jackson**, **Mr Mullet** and **Tommy** appear behind them.*

. . . .

Scene 8

Near Sadie's street, 2.00 a.m.

Mr Jackson	And what time of night is this to be wandering the streets?
Kevin	I'm sorry if you've been worried about Sadie, Mr Jackson, we went to Bangor and missed the last bus . . .
Sadie	And then we got a lift from Kevin's uncle and his car broke down . . .
Tommy	I told you there would be a simple reason for it, Dad.
Mr Jackson	Simple? That's not what I call it . . . We've been searching for hours looking for you . . .
Mr Mullet	The whole street's been right upset and our Linda's nearly up the wall with worrying.
Sadie	Well she'll just need to get down again, won't she!
Mr Mullet	The cheek of it . . .
Mr Jackson	Your mother's in a terrible state. She'll be at the doctor's in the morning . . .
Sadie	Aw she's always at the doctor's . . .
Mr Jackson	*(Going for her)* Why you little . . .

Sadie	*(Jumping clear)* All right, all right . . . I'm coming home now anyway, but I'm not going to be marched up the street as if I was being taken to jail.
Mr Mullet	Jail would be too good for you. *(To Mr Jackson)* Sorry, Jim, but there's times a man must speak his mind. We've nearly been round the bend these last few hours thinking of all the things that might have happened to you.
Sadie	Oh, did you think the Micks had got hold of me and tarred and feathered me?★
Kevin	*(Under his breath)* Sadie!
Mr Mullet	I wouldn't put anything past that lot.
Kevin	Sadie, I'll be seeing you, okay?
Mr Jackson	You just hold your horses, young fella, I'm not finished with you yet.
Tommy	Oh come on, let's get home to bed. We've found Sadie and that's the main thing.
Mr Jackson	That's not the main thing at all. You two go home, I've got some unfinished business with this Mick.
Tommy	Da, you're not going to start fighting.
Mr Jackson	You don't seem to care who your sister's roaming around with till all hours of the night, but I do!
Sadie	What do you want to fight Kevin for? He didn't force me to go with him . . .
Kevin	I don't want to fight anyone, Mr Jackson.
Mr Mullet	No, 'cause you're probably too yellow! You lot are all the same!

★ Tarring and feathering involves smearing a person with tar and then covering him/her with feathers. It is used by Republicans as a method of 'punishing' or frightening people.

Tommy	For heaven's sake, let's go home.

Kevin grabs Mr Mullet by the collar. Mullet is taken off guard – he's not really too keen on doing the fighting himself.

Kevin	Oh you think we're yellow, do you? If you were my own age I'd let you have it, but I don't pick on old men!
Mr Jackson	Why you ... *(He grabs at Kevin, pushing Mullet out of the way)* By the time I'm finished with you, you won't dare come near my daughter again ...
Sadie	*(Pushing in between her father and Kevin)* If you want to fight Kevin you'll have to take me on first!
Kevin	I don't need you to fight my battles, Sadie.
Mr Jackson	I'm going to break every bone in your body, McCoy!

Everyone is struggling ... Tommy gets in between his father and Kevin and holds his father back.

Tommy	*(Almost screaming)* Are you crazy? Break it up! If this goes on any longer we'll have half the neighbourhood out on the streets ... there's a mob gathering already up the road ... we'll have a riot on our hands in a minute! Kevin, you'd best get out of here fast.
Sadie	Tommy's right. Goodnight, Kevin. *(Panicking)* I said goodnight, Kevin!
Kevin	Okay, okay ... goodnight Sadie, Tommy ... *(He looks at Mr Jackson, then says ...)* Goodnight.

He walks away to the other side of the acting area.

Mr Jackson	*(Shouts)* If I see you near my daughter again, I'll kill you!
Tommy	*(Leading his father off)* All right, Da ... that's enough. Let's go.

Mr Mullet   Tommy's right, Jim, let's leave it be for now.

*Tommy leads his father away, **Mr Jackson** still shouting at Kevin... **Mullet** follows them. Just before they go off they freeze: **Mr Jackson** is looking back at Kevin threatening him, **Tommy** is trying to restrain him. **Kevin**, now at the other side of the acting area, has his back to them. **Sadie** moves away from her father then addresses her next speech out to the audience.*

Sadie   I've never seen my father so angry. Through the anger and coldness in his face, I could see he was frightened... he wasn't frightened of Kevin, it was more what he represented. That night my father became a stranger to me.

Mr Jackson, Tommy and Mullet go off stage, then Sadie follows them.

Kevin   *(To audience)* I was lucky to get away before anyone else joined in. Sadie and I had arranged to meet again the next day by the River Lagan but after the little dust-up with her father I thought she might not want to risk it... my most immediate problem was trying to get home in one piece...

Sound of an explosion, gunfire, shouting etc. A soldier comes running on...

Soldier   *(Shouts)* Get down on the ground, son! You want to get killed?

Kevin   *(Obeys)* What in the names's going on?

Soldier   Have you seen anyone running past you?

Kevin   I haven't seen anything.

Soldier   Aye and if you had, you wouldn't be saying! *(Going)* You keep your head down for the next few minutes until you get an all clear...

Kevin   Oh sure, anything you say!

*The soldier runs off, **Brian Rafferty** creeps up behind **Kevin** and puts a finger to his neck as if it was a gun...*

Brian	It's all go tonight, eh Kevin?
Kevin	*(Turning round)* Brian! What are you doing creeping up on me like that?
Brian	*(Laughs)* You've missed all the action. Doyle's Bar got hit by the Prods. But don't worry, they're going to pay for this. They'd burn us out to the last man if we let them.
Kevin	We do a bit of burning ourselves.
Brian	I don't like the sound of that talk.
Kevin	What good does burning things do? I'm sick of fires.
Brian	So you take yourself off to Bangor for the day?
Kevin	How do you know that?
Brian	Your Uncle Albert's got a loose tongue. He told me all about your little trip to the seaside, with your little blonde girl called Sadie.
Kevin	So what?
Brian	Think I'm daft? Only thing he didn't tell me, probably 'cause he didn't have the sense to know, was your little blonde girl was a Prod!
Kevin	It's none of your business.
Brian	I remember Sadie all right, a fine little Loyalist!
Kevin	You won't tell me what to do, Rafferty, so don't even think it.
Brian	No? Oh, well, we'll see... *(Laughs)* Take care going home, Kevin, these are dangerous times!

***Brian** goes off quickly. Music.*

Scene 9

River Lagan, Sunday evening. **Kevin** *stays on from the previous scene.*

Kevin	*(To audience)* Belfast is a really beautiful city. We've got all these parks: Dixon Park, Barnett Park, Clement Wilson Park . . . Don't ask me who Clement Wilson was, I haven't got a clue . . . We've got the Botanic Gardens . . . we even have a rose festival every July . . . So if we're not planting bombs, we're planting flowers . . . It's a very romantic city, believe me!

Sadie joins Kevin.

Sadie	*(To audience)* On Sunday night Kevin and I met by the River Lagan as arranged. We were both a bit shaken by the confrontation with my father . . .
Kevin	*(Hands Sadie a single rose)* Here . . .
Sadie	*(Smells it)* Very nice.
Kevin	*(In fun)* Does your mother know you're out?
Sadie	*(Laughs)* I'm always out. I hate being stuck in the house. *(Pause)* So you got home all right last night?
Kevin	Sure. No problem.
Sadie	I was worried about you.
Kevin	*(Smiles)* I wasn't sure if you were going to come tonight.
Sadie	Nothing's going to put me off seeing you.
Kevin	You mean it, Sadie?
Sadie	You know I do.
Kevin	Well, no one's going to put me off either.
Sadie	Good. All the same I'd better not be too late tonight.
Kevin	No. We don't want to give your father heart failure.

Sadie	*(Laughs)* My father! What was he like last night? I'm sorry about all that, Kevin.
Kevin	Forget it. Parents are all the same.
Sadie	I wonder what you'll be like as a father.
Kevin	Me? I've never really thought about it.
Sadie	Maybe we can't help ending up like our parents . . . I mean you're sort of brain-washed from the day you're born.
Kevin	Yeh, a lot of it's subconscious, you don't even know it's happening to you and then one day you end up talking just like them . . .
Sadie	Frightening, isn't it?
Kevin	You're telling me!
Sadie	You always notice it more in other people . . . Linda Mullet, she's a classic case, she's even beginning to look like her mother, and I thought they'd thrown away the mould after she was born!
Kevin	*(Laughs)* It's funny, you and Linda used to be friends.
Sadie	Oh I don't know, you sort of grow apart don't you?
Kevin	Yeh, you can say that again. I mean see our street, I used to love it when I was a kid but now it drives me up the wall.
Sadie	Same here. Aw it's great everyone knowing each other, but it gets really claustrophobic everyone knowing your business as well. I mean if you go into our corner shop, you know, Mrs McConkey's, you don't need to buy a newspaper, that woman's better informed than the BBC . . . she knows more about my family that I do!
Kevin	D'you think you'd ever want to leave Belfast?
Sadie	I don't know. Not for good. I'd like to travel though, see what's going on in the rest of the world.

Kevin	I wouldn't mind that myself . . . about the furthest I've been is Dublin, can you believe it? We've got some cousins down there . . .
Sadie	I wouldn't mind going to America or even China, somewhere really different, you know.
Kevin	Maybe we should explore the world together . . .
Sadie	Set out on the high seas?
Kevin	Something like that.
Sadie	Only one problem, what do we do for money?
Kevin	Good question.
Sadie	Oh well, no harm in dreaming.
Kevin	You never know, Sadie, one of these days.
Sadie	Sure. *(She looks at her watch)* Shall we meet here again tomorrow?
Kevin	*(Putting on 'Bogart' accent)* Same place, same time!
Sadie	Half seven.
Kevin	*(Looks at his watch)* Only nineteen hours, twenty-five minutes and three seconds away!
Sadie	*(To audience)* We parted before we got to my street, we didn't want to risk meeting my father again . . . *(Exit)*
Kevin	*(To audience)* I was in a bit of dream all the way home. You know the sort of thing, on cloud nine, not even looking where I was going . . . all I could think of was meeting Sadie again and both of us wandering along arm in arm by the side of the river . . .

Suddenly two people, their faces hidden by balaclavas, rush at Kevin from either side of the stage. One of them is **Brian.**

Brian	All right, McCoy, your number's up!

Kevin	Ah! Get off . . . what's going on?
Brian	This is how we deal with traitors . . .

> *Kevin is beaten up violently. The job done,*
> ***Brian** and his **friend** run off, leaving*
> ***Kevin** groaning in agony . . . after a few*
> *minutes, **Kevin** gathers the strength to*
> *struggle off stage.*

. . . .

Scene 10

A cafe, Belfast city centre, Monday
*6.00 p.m. **Sadie** enters and places two*
chairs at a table. She sits with her head in
*her hands. **Brede** comes on with two cups*
of coffee. She sits at the table. She places
one of the cups near Sadie, then touches
*Sadie gently on the arm. **Sadie** looks up at*
Brede.

Sadie	Was he badly hurt, Brede?
Brede	A lot of bruises, cuts on his head and leg. He got three stitches in his head.
Sadie	Oh God . . .
Brede	Mr Kelly found him lying unconscious outside the yard late last night. He called an ambulance and Kevin got carted off to hospital.
Sadie	Which hospital is he in?
Brede	They let him out this morning.
Sadie	It happened because of me, didn't it?
Brede	*(Quietly)* Yes, I think so.
Sadie	D'you know who did it?

Brede	There were a couple of them. One of them was Brian Rafferty.
Sadie	I thought he was Kevin's friend.
Brede	It just shows you, doesn't it.
Sadie	Did Kevin ask you to come and tell me?
Brede	He doesn't know I'm here. He's going to meet you tonight as planned. He'll not let you down. But . . . I've come to ask you not to meet him.
Sadie	You want me to let him down?
Brede	It might be best. He's too proud to try and see you again if you don't see him. I know it's hard, but it would be easier if he thought you'd given in.

Pause. **Sadie** *is fighting back her tears.*

Sadie . . . I'm sorry.

Sadie	I don't know, Brede, I don't know . . . I don't know anything at all. I want to see Kevin and he wants to see me and all these people are getting between us . . . Is it right for me to give in to Brian Rafferty and his friends? Is it?
Brede	You don't want Kevin to be hurt again, do you?
Sadie	You know it's funny . . . people say I'm my own worst enemy . . . I make trouble for myself. They say you should go out with one of your own kind, it's easier, less aggravation . . . Well for goodness sake you're all missing the point, aren't you . . . I'm not going out with Kevin because he's a Catholic, or a Mick or whatever you want to call him . . . I'm going out with him because he's Kevin . . . We like being with each other, we don't want to be with anyone else. I mean I could have met a Protestant and felt the same way about him as I do about Kevin, but it didn't happen like that, did it? If I meet Kevin he might get beaten up again, if I don't he'll hate me . . . What sort of choice is that for anyone? I just want a laugh, I want a bit of fun . . . I just want us to be walking out together, just the two of us, sharing things, spending time together . . . Why can't we do that?

Brede	There's times when it might be all right for a Catholic boy to be walking out with a Protestant girl, but now's not one of them.
Sadie	It's not much to ask to want to walk by the river with someone you like . . . I'm not sure. I can't promise, Brede. How can I promise never to see Kevin again? I have to think about it.
Brede	Think carefully then. There's enough blood, Sadie, without any more getting shed.

> **Brede** *exits, leaving* **Sadie** *alone on stage.*
> **Sadie** *starts to drink her coffee, then puts it down and pushes the cup away . . .*

Sadie	*(Almost to herself)* I'm sorry, Kevin, you've got to believe me, I'm really sorry . . .

> *She rushes off in tears.*
> *Music. Optional: We see more scenes of Belfast. At first they are all 'tourist'-type pictures – the City Hall, the parks, etc. Then we see a couple of pictures of a street blocked off by soldiers and the RUC . . .*

Scene 11

By the River Lagan, Monday evening.
Kevin *enters and sits down stage. His head is bandaged and his arm is in a wrist sling. He is short of breath and finds it an effort to move much . . . He looks at his watch, then looks around . . . no sign of Sadie yet.*

Kevin *(Partly to audience, partly to himself)* If this is what friends do to you, who needs enemies . . . *(Putting on voice)* Take it easy, Mr McCoy, stay off your work for the next few days. Oh, I'm sure ould man Kelly would love that! I'm not the type to sit about the house, it'd be like being in prison. Besides I want to see Sadie . . . *(Looks at his watch)* She'll get a bit of a fright when she sees me like this . . . *(He puts his hand to his head. It's obviously hurting badly.)* She's never normally late, I don't understand it . . . Come on, Sadie, where are you, girl? *(Puts his head in his hands, groans.)*

*At this point an elderly gentleman enters. It is **Mr Blake**. He stands for a few seconds, lighting his pipe, then he notices **Kevin** . . . **Kevin** continues to groan quietly, unaware that he is being watched. He's finding it difficult to keep his head up . . . **Mr Blake** moves towards him, warily at first, then more determined.*

Mr Blake Excuse me . . . are you all right?

Kevin Mm?

Mr Blake You look in a bad way.

Kevin *(Recovering a bit)* No, I'm fine . . . really . . .

Mr Blake Have you been here long?

Kevin I'm all right, really, I'm waiting on someone . . .

Mr Blake You don't look all right to me . . . it looks as if there's blood seeping through that bandage . . .

Kevin	It's okay . . . I'm fine . . . just a bit weak . . . had a bit of an accident last night . . .
Mr Blake	Should you be out and about so soon? Perhaps I could get you to a doctor, just to check that bandage . . . my car's not far away . . .

Kevin looks at his watch again.

Kevin	What time do you make it?
Mr Blake	Nearly eight o'clock.
Kevin	Are you sure?
Mr Blake	Is she late then? A woman's prerogative, eh?
Kevin	She's never late.
Mr Blake	Maybe she's not coming.
Kevin	She'll come.
Mr Blake	You sound pretty sure.
Kevin	Well . . . I know her.
Mr Blake	I should hope so. *(Smiles)* Nice spot this. I used to come here when I was courting . . . a long time ago . . . it was one of our favourite meeting places, Elizabeth always loved the river . . .
Kevin	Sadie probably got delayed, but she'll be here, I know . . .
Mr Blake	Even after we were married, we'd come here of an evening . . . Look, son, I'll make a deal with you. You're not looking well at all. I'll walk along the path a bit and then I'll come back, and if your young lady hasn't turned up I'll give you a lift home, eh?
Kevin	All right.
Mr Blake	Whereabouts d'you live?

Kevin   *(Sighs)* Look, it's very kind of you to offer, but I might as well tell you, I'm a Catholic.

Mr Blake   *(Shrugs his shoulders)* And I might as well tell you, I'm not. But if you think that means I'm going to drop you by the side of the river, you've got another thing coming. I'll be back in a few minutes, all right?

Kevin   Sure.

> As **Mr Blake** *starts to walk off,* **Sadie** *comes rushing on and bumps into him. She recognises him.*

Sadie   Oh sorry . . . Mr Blake? What are you doing here?

Mr Blake   Well, well, Sadie Jackson!

Sadie   *(Seeing Kevin)* Kevin! Oh Kevin, I'm sorry I'm late . . .

Kevin   Sadie!

Sadie   What have they done to you?

Kevin   I'm all right, Sadie, it looks worse than it is . . . and this gentleman's been looking after me.

Mr Blake   So that's who you were waiting on, Sadie Jackson, well, well . . . it's a funny old world.

Kevin   You two know each other?

Sadie   Mr Blake was one of my teachers. Haven't seen you for ages, Mr Blake.

Mr Blake   *(Smiles)* Things have been pretty quiet since you left. Now that young fella of yours looks as if he needs to rest up somewhere and have a good strong cup of tea. I've got my car along the road, why don't you both come back to my place and join me for some tea?

Sadie   Sounds like a good idea to me, Kevin.

Kevin	Okay.
Mr Blake	*(Helping **Kevin** up)* I'll give my doctor a ring and get him to have a look at your dressings. He's an old friend and I'm sure he'll oblige . . .

They go off . . . ***Sadie*** *stays behind.*

Sadie	*(To audience)* Mr Blake was really good. He took us to his house in one of the posher districts of Belfast . . . well, posh compared with us. He'd just retired from teaching and he lived in a little bungalow, really nicely done out . . . He left me and Kevin alone in the lounge while he made the tea. *(By now **Kevin** has re-appeared.)*
Kevin	He's all right, isn't he?
Sadie	Aw, he's really nice. We used to call him 'Twinkle Blake' at school because of his eyes. He was one of these teachers everybody liked, always really friendly and open . . . Kevin, I'm sorry I was late. You see Brede came to see me . . .
Kevin	Brede? Oh, I see . . . she asked you not to come, didn't she?
Sadie	Yes. She was worried about you and I didn't know what to do. But I couldn't bear the thought of you waiting.
Kevin	I'm glad.
Sadie	The thing is, Kevin, I decided I'd come to see you tonight, but I decided it would have to be the last time.
Kevin	Sadie, what are you talking about?
Sadie	It's not because I don't want to see you. You know I do.
Kevin	But you're going to give in to them?
Sadie	It's not a case of giving in.
Kevin	All right, what is it then?
Sadie	I don't want you to get hurt again, that's all.

Kevin	*(Sighs)* I'm sorry, I didn't mean to sound angry with you. It's just that I hate the idea of Brian Rafferty telling me what to do.
Sadie	It's not just Brian Rafferty. If it wasn't him, it would be somebody else. Every time I left you I'd be wondering if you were going to be beaten up on the way home.
Kevin	We could meet in secret.
Sadie	Yes, but where?
Kevin	Oh, I don't know.

> ***Mr Blake*** *enters with a tray of tea and biscuits.*

Mr Blake	Here we are, some tea, and the doctor's on his way, okay?
Sadie	Thanks.
Mr Blake	You two don't look very happy.
Kevin	We're not.
Mr Blake	Here, have some tea, Kevin ... Now do you want to tell me what this is all about?
Sadie	D'you think we're mad, Mr Blake, going out with each other?
Mr Blake	*(Takes a deep breath)* Yes. And I should probably give you good advice and tell you to give it up. You can't always walk with the crowd, especially if you don't like the way they're walking. I admire you for it. It takes a bit of courage. You were never lacking in that, Sadie.
Sadie	There was a time when I wouldn't go near a Catholic ...
Mr Blake	And now here you are going out with one. Sadie, people are just people, and there's good and bad on all sides.
Sadie	But if me going out with Kevin causes so much trouble, is it worth it?

Mr Blake	Only you and Kevin can decide that. If you really like each other you'll find a way to keep going and, with a bit of luck, in time, everyone will leave you alone. Look, I think you need a few days to recover from all this, both of you. It's not just Kevin's injuries, it's the shock of being attacked.
Sadie	I know, I just can't think straight at the moment.
Kevin	You're not the only one.
Mr Blake	I tell you what, why don't the two of you come round here for supper later in the week?
Sadie	We'd love to, wouldn't we, Kevin?
Kevin	If you don't mind, Mr Blake.
Mr Blake	We'll make it Friday, that'll give you a bit of time to rest and get your strength back . . . and no one will bother you out here. Okay?
Kevin	Sure.
Mr Blake	All right, I'll clear this away.

Mr Blake takes the tray and the mugs and exits.

Sadie	Well, Kevin, I'll see you on Friday then?
Kevin	Yeh. *(They smile.)* Sadie, don't you worry, I'll be okay.
Sadie	You take it easy, all right? I want you fit and well for Friday.

Kevin goes off.

Scene 12   *Sadie's street*

Sadie   *(To audience)* It was hard not seeing Kevin until Friday. I was wondering what he was getting up to. I couldn't phone him or anything. I just had to be patient. Was he seeing Kate Kelly? She always used to fancy him. After all it would be a lot easier for him to go out with one of his own kind.

                   Police and fire engine sirens. **Tommy** *comes running on.*

Tommy   Sadie! Have you see what's going on outside?

Sadie   What are you talking about?

Tommy   It's Mrs McConkey's shop. It's on fire!

                   Sadie and Tommy run to another part of the acting area and stand watching the fire (perhaps from behind the barrier). We hear the sound of people shouting, sirens etc. Mr and Mrs Jackson, Mr and Mrs Mullet and Linda Mullet plus other neighbours come on and stand in groups staring at the fire.

Mrs Jackson   God help us all, it could be our turn next.

Mrs Mullet   And to think I was only in there a few hours ago . . .

Mr Mullet   Don't you worry, whoever was behind this will soon pay for it.

Mr Jackson   Oh yeh, if they ever find them.

Mrs Mullet   It's funny, there was a young girl in there when I was in. She wasn't from round here.

Mr Jackson   You think she had something to do with it?

Mrs Mullet   Well, you never know do you?

Sadie   Tommy, I don't believe this, we've been going in there for years and look at it, just a mass of flames.

Tommy	They say it was a petrol bomb . . .
Sadie	Well, Mrs McConkey's shop's a goner for sure . . .
Tommy	Let's hope she's not . . .
Sadie	You mean she was in there?
Tommy	Oh yeh, she was in the back shop doing her stock-taking . . .
Sadie	Oh my God . . .
Tommy	They've taken her to hospital. God knows how they got her out.
Mr Jackson	There's not much we can do here.
Mrs Jackson	I think we need a good strong cup of tea after all this.
Mr Mullet	Nice of you to offer . . .

> *Mrs Jackson frowns. She hadn't meant to invite the Mullets. They all go off except* **Linda. Linda** *joins* **Sadie** *and* **Tommy** *at the barrier.*

Linda	Hello, Sadie, Tommy . . .
Sadie	Oh hi, Linda. I might have known you'd be here, never miss a show, eh?
Linda	And I'm surprised you're not out with your Mick boyfriend tonight.
Sadie	It's none of your business.
Linda	Maybe it is my business . . .
Tommy	Look, Linda, just drop it, right?
Linda	Maybe there's more to this than meets the eye.
Sadie	What are you talking about?

Linda   Call it coincidence, call it what you like . . . When my mother was in there earlier having a blether with Mrs McConkey, there was a girl in there, a stranger, looking for you, Sadie . . .

Tommy   Sadie, what's she talking about?

Sadie   I've no idea.

Linda   Oh yes, you have. 'Cause you know as well as I do who that stranger was . . . it was Kevin McCoy's sister, Brede.

Tommy   Well, what's Brede got to do with this?

Linda   You never know. You don't get many Catholics coming round here do you?

Sadie   Are you suggesting that Brede might have put a bomb in Mrs McConkey's shop?

Linda   Not exactly, but she could have been sent to spy out the lie of the land.

Tommy   Linda, don't be stupid. Brede wouldn't have anything to do with this. You know something Linda, you're just like your mother, you talk a lot of rubbish!

                 Tommy *goes off, followed by* ***Linda.***

Linda   *(Going)* Tommy, I never thought I'd hear you talking to me like that . . . Tommy, all I meant was . . .

Sadie   To be honest, Linda, I don't know what Tommy sees in you! *(To audience)* Mrs McConkey died. We all knew she had been badly injured . . . but . . . well, it was terrible seeing it on a newspaper stand the next morning . . . 'SHOP BURNED DOWN. WOMAN DEAD'. It was so anonymous, so cold, so detached from reality . . . it wasn't just any old shop, it wasn't just a woman . . . it was Mrs McConkey . . . we used to make fun of her, call her names . . .

                 Sadie *moves away from the barrier and sits on one of the chairs, still shocked by the news of Mrs McConkey's death.*

Scene 13

*Mr Blake's house. **Sadie** is still on stage from the previous scene. **Mr Blake** comes on and gives her a cup of tea.*

Mr Blake   Here, Sadie, drink this.

Sadie   It's been quite a day, Mr Blake.

Mr Blake   I know.

Sadie   I'm sorry for landing on your doorstep like this, but I didn't know where else to go.

Mr Blake   Shouldn't you be at work?

Sadie   Oh, I've been there all right, for the last time. Some of the girls had seen me with Kevin and it got back to the supervisor . . . she's a right old bitch, so today she started asking all sorts of questions, being really nasty about Kevin . . . I told her to get lost, I told her to mind her own business. So that was that, I lost my job. Now I don't know what I'm going to do.

Mr Blake   I tell you what, until you get something better you can work for me.

Sadie   For you?

Mr Blake   Yes, I could do with a bit of help around here, cleaning and cooking. It'd only be part-time, but it would help me out and maybe help you out as well.

Sadie   Are you serious, Mr Blake?

Mr Blake   *(Going off)* The job's yours if you want it.

Sadie   Wait till I tell my mother I've lost one job and got another all in the same day . . .

*Mr Blake has now gone off stage. **Sadie** stays on and **Kevin** comes on stage.*

Kevin	*(To audience)* I fell into the habit of meeting Sadie at Mr Blake's. Sometimes we'd spend the afternoon sitting in the garden, all three of us chatting, other times Sadie and I would find ourselves going off for long walks . . .
Sadie	*(To audience)* These were the good times . . .

• •

Scene 14

*A park near Mr Blake's house. **Kevin** and **Sadie** walk down towards the front of the acting area.*

Kevin	It's nice being able to walk about without having to look over our shoulders all the time.
Sadie	Well, no one knows us round here.
Kevin	Back home I feel I'm being followed all the time . . .
Sadie	Well, at least you don't need to worry about that here.

__Kate Kelly__ appears upstage. She watches Kevin and Sadie.

Kevin	I'd better be going now, I'll see you tomorrow.
Sadie	Yeh. I'd better be getting home as well. See you tomorrow?
Kevin	*(Smiles)* What do you think?

__Kevin__ and __Sadie__ embrace and part. __Kevin__ smiles.

Sadie	*(Going)* See you!

__Sadie__ goes off, __Kevin__ turns to go off in the opposite direction and meets __Kate__.

Kate	Long time no see, Kevin.

Kevin	Kate!
Kate	You're so mysterious these days, I mean what do you do with yourself all day? You don't seem to have time for your old friends these days.
Kevin	Some of them are no longer my friends. I don't particularly like getting beaten up.
Kate	It wouldn't be friends who did that.
Kevin	Kate, I know who did it.
Kate	You're thinking of Brian Rafferty, aren't you? He says you've been going around slandering him. He's not pleased.
Kevin	I don't care if he's pleased or not. You keep out of it, Kate. Now if you don't mind I'd like to get home.
Kate	Just a minute, Kevin. I want to know something.
Kevin	What?
Kate	Is it all over with us?
Kevin	Kate . . . it's not as if we were going steady or anything.
Kate	I thought we were.
Kevin	Well I didn't.
Kate	Who is she?
Kevin	Look, Kate, you've got it all wrong . . .
Kate	Oh have I?
Kevin	We were just friends. I thought you understood that . . .
Kate	Oh I understand all right, Kevin.
Kevin	Good.

Kate You're cruel and horrible, Kevin McCoy, and I hate you! *(Screams)* I hate you!

> *Kate runs off. Kevin looks confused and slightly stunned. He sits down and puts his head in his hands. Music.*

. . . .

Scene 15

> *Kevin's street. Kevin remains sitting with his head in his hands. Sadie appears on the other side of the acting area.*

Sadie *(To audience)* It wasn't easy going out with Kevin . . . I mean we got on well and everything . . . oh sure, we had arguments from time to time, I'm not denying it, but it was all the other pressures that made it difficult . . . My parents wanting to know where I was all the time; the gossiping tongues, people that used to be my friends. the threats, oh yes, I got them too . . . sometimes I couldn't sleep at nights for thinking about it . . .

> *We hear Sadie dreaming. The voices are distorted, maybe with an echo effect . . . Sadie closes her eyes trying to shut out the voices . . . [This scene could be done as a dream sequence using voice-overs on tape, or it could be done 'live' with Linda and Steve and later on Brede and Brian actually onstage saying their lines.]*

Linda *(Voice-over)* Not out with your Mick boyfriend the night, Sadie?

Sadie *(Voice-over)* I've nothing to talk to you about, Linda Mullet.

Linda You needn't pretend you don't know who I'm talking about.

Steve Will you be marching on the Twelfth, Sadie?

Linda Her Mick boyfriend won't let her.

Sadie Just leave me alone!

Steve   *(Voice-over)* Course her brother's not much better ... won't even join the Lodge ...

Sadie   Leave Tommy out of it ... Just leave us alone!

Sadie   *(To audience)* I wasn't the only one having trouble sleeping. Kevin didn't tell me at first but he was having nightmares as well ... and sometimes the dreams became reality ...

Sadie exits.

Brede   *(Voice-over)* Have you been upsetting Kate again?

Kevin   She upset herself.

Brede   Kate Kelly can cause trouble ... she's been hanging around with Brian Rafferty a lot ...

Kevin   Maybe they'll be good for each other ...

Brian   Kevin! There was a time when you were ready to fight for one Ireland ... There's no other way, Kevin! No other way! There's times you have to stand up and be counted!

> *Suddenly the music and effects stop and two British **soldiers** burst on to the stage. One of them grabs **Kevin** and hauls him to his feet.*

Soldier 1   All right, on your feet, sonny!

Kevin   What the hell's going on?

Soldier 2   Kevin McCoy?

Kevin   Eh?

Soldier 1   That's him all right.

Kevin   Look, what do you want?

Soldier 2   We've got something to show you ... I think it's something you lost.

Kevin	I don't know what you're talking about . . .

*One of the **soldiers** holds up a rifle covered with a blanket.*

Soldier 2	Guess what we've got in here . . .
Kevin	Eh?
Soldier 1	Oh, little Mick's playing dumb . . . playing little games with us . . . oh well, want to see what we've got?
Kevin	Do what you like, it's got nothing to do with me!
Soldier 2	I think it might, son.

*The **soldier** takes off the blanket and holds the rifle in front of Kevin.*

Surprise, surprise! Looks familiar, eh?

Kevin	What's that got to do with me?
Soldier 1	So you're saying it's not yours?
Kevin	What would I want with a rifle?
Soldier 2	Oh, I couldn't possibly imagine. *(Grabs him)* All right, if it's not yours, whose is it?
Kevin	*(Shouts)* I don't know.
Soldier 1	Well, it was found at Kelly's Scrapyard where you work.
Kevin	Hard luck, I've been off work for the past week. Now, if you don't mind, I'd like to go home.
Soldier 1	You're a bit of a comedian, aren't you? Come on, let's get him down to the barracks . . .
Kevin	Leave off . . . I've done nothing wrong I'm telling you . . .

*They drag him off stage. **Brede** comes on.*

Brede	*(To audience)* They questioned my brother all through the night. I went to the barracks and told them about Kate Kelly and how she had a grudge against Kevin. Kate's evidence against Kevin was pretty weak anyway. She thought she saw Kevin hiding the rifle in the yard. But Kate wasn't the real culprit, it was Brian Rafferty. They say revenge is sweet . . .
	*Kevin re-appears, **Brede** looks at him sympathetically, he returns her look and walks past her to **Sadie** who has now appeared at the other side of the acting area.*
Kevin	I waited in the alley for him this morning, Sadie. I was like a killer stalking my victim. I got him all right. I let him have it, it was as if the devil was in me, I just kept on hitting him . . .
Sadie	You didn't kill him did you?
Kevin	No, but I could have.
	***Brede** goes off stage.*
Kevin	Do you think I was wrong to go after him?
Sadie	I don't know what good it does. But it's what you think that counts.
Kevin	I don't know what I think. I felt sick when I stood and looked down at him. It's not that I care very much about Brian. I wanted to fight him, but after I'd got him down there lying at my feet, I wished I hadn't done it. I'd sunk to his level. It was as if I'd been stained by the very thing that's been making me sick . . . All this meaningless revenge . . . what good does it do? I mean what's next on the agenda? More blood?
	Pause.
Kevin	*(To audience)* Sadie and I spent a lot of time at Mr Blake's. Sometimes all three of us would get in his car and go for a run in the country, we'd take a picnic, make a day of it . . .
	Music.

Scene 16

In the country. **Mr Blake** *and* **Sadie** *are lying on a blanket. They take some food out of a picnic hamper.* **Kevin** *sits beside them. Conversation is in full flow. Music fades ...*

Sadie	My mum's that worried about me, she's been trying to fix me up with a job ...
Mr Blake	Well, it shows how much she cares, Sadie.
Sadie	It's the butcher round the corner, they were wanting someone on the cash desk. Can you imagine me sitting in a butcher's shop all day long?
Mr Blake	Well, at least it's a job, Sadie.
Sadie	Not for me.
Kevin	So how did you get out of it?
Sadie	Well, I went in to see the manager, just to please my mother you know ... and I told him I was a vegetarian and the sight of blood makes me boke!

They all burst out laughing.

Sadie	He said that under the circumstances it might not be the best job for me!
Kevin	Trust you, Sadie!
Mr Blake	Ah it's nice to hear you two laughing. Whatever happens we mustn't forget how to laugh.
Kevin	I bet your mother was furious.
Sadie	She was raging, she's not been into the butcher's for days.
Mr Blake	Aw well ...
Sadie and Kevin	*(Together slightly sending Mr Blake up)* ... I suppose we'd better be getting home, after all it is getting late ...

	Mr Blake laughs and they gather up the picnic and start towards the car.
Sadie	Thanks for bringing us.
Mr Blake	It's my pleasure, we must come again . . .
	Suddenly they freeze as we hear the following news report . . .
Newsreader	*(Voice-over)* BBC Radio Ulster News at six o'clock. Police are tonight investigating an accident on the Antrim road in which a retired Belfast school teacher and his two passengers were injured when their car left the road. Police suspect that the wheels of the car were deliberately loosened causing the car to veer out of control . . .
	Mr Blake exits, Sadie and Kevin stay where they are.
Sadie	*(To audience)* After the crash we decided not to go on meeting at Mr Blake's. It was too dangerous. I went on working for him, cooking and cleaning and waiting for Kevin to phone to arrange our next meeting . . .
Kevin	*(To audience)* I had decided not to phone.
	He goes off.

• •

Scene 17

	Sadie's house, the twelfth day of July. We can hear the bands playing and marching outside. Sadie is sitting trying to write a letter to Kevin . . .
Sadie	*(To herself)* 'Dear Kevin, Today's the Twelfth, almost three weeks since I last saw you. The Orange bands are driving me mad, just like they used to drive you mad . . .'

She crumples up the letter. **Tommy** *comes in quietly.*

Tommy	Sadie? Sadie, is there anything wrong?
Sadie	No, Tommy. Everything's fine, just fine.
Tommy	I'm going to watch the parade, would you like to come?
Sadie	That's the last thing I want to do.
Tommy	Dad was on at me again this morning about joining the Lodge.
Sadie	Are you going to? That's it, Tommy, join up and be a good Orangeman and make everyone happy . . . They might even give you a bowler hat if you're lucky.
Tommy	I said no.
Sadie	Good on you, Tommy, I though we'd lost you.
Tommy	There's no harm in watching the parade though. It keeps Dad happy, at least he thinks I'm showing a bit of interest.
Sadie	Well, I'm going to get as far away from here as possible. I'm going to Bangor.
Tommy	Who with?
Sadie	Don't worry, I haven't seen Kevin for weeks.

Tommy *walks off.*

Scene 18

Banger. Music in the background. **Kevin** *comes on from the opposite side of the acting area to* **Sadie** ...

Kevin *(To audience)* I went to Bangor for the day ... you see the year I met Sadie we'd spent the Twelfth there ...

Sadie *(To* **Kevin***)* I thought I might bump into you ...

They smile and move towards each other.

Kevin *(To audience)* We started seeing one another again ...

Sadie *(To audience)* We went back to meeting at Mr Blake's ...

Kevin *(To audience)* We tried to be careful ...

Sadie *(To audience)* For a while we thought we were going to get away with it ...

Kevin We should have known better ...

Kevin walks slowly off. As he does so, Tommy comes back on.

•••

Scene 19

Sadie's room. **Sadie** *stands in the same position as in the scene before. She is very still* ... **Tommy** *moves towards her* ...

Tommy Sadie, I've got some bad news ... Mr Blake's neighbour phoned ...

Sadie You mean Moira? ... Tommy ... what's happened?

Tommy ... It's Mr Blake ... he's dead.

Sadie No!

He puts his arms round her, she doesn't move.

Tommy	Someone threw a petrol bomb into his house last night. The place went up in minutes and he didn't have a chance ... I'm sorry, Sadie ... I'm sorry ...
Sadie	*(In tears)* Oh God ... it's my fault, Tommy ... it's all my fault ...
Tommy	You mustn't say that ...
Sadie	It's true ...

Sadie *moves away from* **Tommy.**

Sadie	I shouldn't have let him get involved, we shouldn't have spent so much time at his house ... Remember when we were at school ... people used to make fun of Mr Blake ... they liked him, but they gave him a hard time. He always took it in good spirits, he was never one to hold a grudge ... he was nice, wasn't he? Too nice for his own good maybe ... if it hadn't been for him, Kevin and I would have split up long ago ... I once asked him why he was helping Kevin and me ... he said that we deserved a chance, he said that we had a right to be together ... he gave us hope ...

During the speech, **Tommy** *exits and by the end of it* **Kevin** *has come on and stands beside* **Sadie.** *As* **Tommy** *and* **Kevin** *pass each other they exchange a glance.* **Kevin** *has a suitcase with him ... we are now at Belfast docks ...*

Scene 20

Belfast docks, midday. **Kevin** *is standing by* **Sadie,** *holding his suitcase.*

Kevin	I've had enough, Sadie ... I never thought I'd see the day when I'd want to leave Belfast ... But I'm sick of it all ... sick of all the killings. I keep wondering who put that bomb through Mr Blake's window. Was it one of my so-called friends? Would Brian Rafferty really go that far?
Sadie	It could have been someone I know, someone from my street.

Kevin	What sort of place has this become? I'd like to walk down a street where there were no soldiers with guns, no policemen with their fingers on triggers . . . and no bloody graffiti on the walls . . . there must be more to life than all of that . . .
Sadie	My mother was shouting at me again yesterday. Everything's back to normal. It's nearly a week now since they buried Mr Blake . . . 'Well, Sadie, you've learned your lesson now . . .' that's what she said, no kiddin', and she meant it. My father is convinced it was one of your lot . . . I told him just to go to hell, I said it could just as easily have been him next door, your good friend Mr Mullet . . . I thought he was going to hit me . . . he stood up and came over to me and looked me in the eye . . . but before he could say anything, I started crying, I felt I was going to burst . . . so he didn't hit me, he put his arms round me and held me – that was worse, he was trying to comfort me and I just felt cold all through my body . . . I wish to God he had hit me, it would have made it easier!
Kevin	Parents! My mother thinks I should have taken back my old job at Kelly's, she doesn't want to face up to things . . . I can understand it in a way, they've got to go on living in that street. Brede was all right though, she helped me pack . . . she understands, she knows . . . I'll miss Brede you know, I really will . . . I'll miss Belfast . . . *(Laughs)* I'm feeling homesick already and I'm not even on the ferry . . .
Sadie	Did you think I wouldn't come?
Kevin	I knew you'd be here . . . the only trouble is, I don't want to say goodbye to you . . .
Sadie	Kevin, I haven't come to say goodbye . . .
Kevin	*(Nervous laugh)* No, of course, we'll see each other again.
Sadie	You don't understand, do you? Look, I've bought a ticket, I'm coming with you. That is if you don't mind?
Kevin	Sadie, are you kidding?
Sadie	*(Excited)* I've no luggage. I couldn't walk out of the house with a case, so you'll have to take me as I stand.

Kevin	Sadie, this is the best news I've had in months.

> *He picks her up and swings her round.*
> *They kiss.*

Sadie	*(Smiles)* Come on then, let's get aboard, what are we waiting for?

Kevin	Nothing. London here we come!

> ***Kevin*** *picks up his case and they turn to*
> *go, but freeze. We hear their voices on tape*
> *again with music in the background.*

Sadie	*(Voice-over)* And that was just the beginning . . .

Kevin	*(Voice-over)* You should have seen Sadie on the boat, I've never seen anyone looking so ill in all my life, honestly . . .

Sadie	*(Laughing)* Ssh . . . shut up Kevin . . . you're not meant to tell them about that . . .

> *We hear them both laughing, then this*
> *fades and we hear . . .*

Newsreader	*(Voice-over)* Capital Radio, Newsflash. A bomb has exploded in the centre of London today. It is understood that the explosion was caused by a car bomb. Unconfirmed reports say that at least five people have been killed and over a hundred have been injured. No one has claimed responsibility for the incident but a police spokesman confirmed that eight people have been detained under the Prevention of Terrorism Act. An emergency telephone number has been given for relatives and friends, the number is 01-779 . . . *(Fade)*

> *As the newsflash fades the music comes*
> *up . . .*
> *During the newsflash **Sadie** and **Kevin***
> *turn back to face the audience . . . also the*
> *other members of the cast come back on*
> *stage . . . They all stand motionless as they*
> *hear the news report.*
> *After the newsflash, the music builds, then*
> *fades.*

Activities

Conflict in Ireland

Talk

1   What examples of violence are there in **Across the Barricades?** Make a list of them.

2   Is it clear who is responsible for them? In each case describe the situation as fully as you can on the basis of what you have read.

Research

Find out more about the background to the conflict in Northern Ireland. Try and find answers to these questions.

- When did the British first become involved in Ireland?

- What happened in 1916?

- When was Ireland divided into two parts?

- What is a nationalist?

- What happened in 1969?

- What is the IRA? What does the IRA want?

- What has happened recently in Ireland?

- What possible solutions have been suggested to the 'troubles'?

Task

Read a selection of national newspapers for a week. Cut out any articles about Ireland. Paste them onto paper. How many deal with Northern Ireland? What impression of Ireland do they give?

Write a paragraph to go with your newspaper cuttings, suitable for someone of your own age, in which you describe your impressions.

Religion in Northern Ireland

Sadie And these statues and things, I mean honestly . . . I don't know how you can bring yourself to pray to them.

Kevin What about your lot? Worshipping a silly old Dutchman dead these three hundred years.

Read

One of the causes of the situation in Northern Ireland today is the different religious beliefs of the Catholics and Protestants who live there.

Catholics make up about a third of the population of Northern Ireland, but Protestants are in the minority on the whole island. Most Catholics in Northern Ireland want there to be one united Ireland. They want this to be achieved by peaceful means. So do most people in the Irish Republic.

However, the Protestant majority in Northern Ireland wants to remain part of the United Kingdom and the British Government has promised to support them.

Research

Protestants and Catholics have very different views about some parts of religion and life. Find out as much as you can about these.

Find out what they think about:

- the Pope
- marriage
- priests

On what subjects do you think Catholics and Protestants would agree? Try and talk to Protestants and Catholics in your school, home and community to find out more.

What Do They Mean?

Talk

1 There are a number of words in **Across the Barricades** with which you may not have been familiar. In pairs, find where these words are used in the play. Decide which of the meanings given in the chart below is the correct one.

12th July	admit to things done wrong. Catholics confess their sins to a priest in a part of the church set aside for confession
King Billy	one of a group of girls in a parade, normally dressed up and twirling a baton or playing an instrument
majorette	meeting-place for members of the Orange Order – a society set up by Protestants in the 1790s
loyalist	King William of Orange – a Protestant hero
lodge	Protestants
Micks	The date of the Battle of the Boyne in 1690, when the Protestant William of Orange defeated the Catholic armies of James II. Protestants celebrate this day by marching with bands and banners.
Republican	member of the Orange Order
confess	Catholics
Tarring and feathering	someone who wants to stay part of the United Kingdom
Prods	smearing a person with tar and then covering him/her with feathers. Used by Republicans as a method of 'punishing' or frightening people.
Orangeman	people, mostly Catholics, who want the North to join the South and become part of Eire/the Republic of Ireland

2 Decide to which characters in the play these words apply.

Who Thinks What in the Play

Each of the characters in **Across the Barricades** has his or her own set of opinions, some of which change during the play, some of which remain the same. Decide which of the characters in the play these views might belong to.

A 'My attitudes to living in Belfast have changed fairly drastically over the years. When I was 13, I would never have wanted to leave Belfast. My whole life revolved around being a Protestant and walking on the Twelfth. I probably would still be marching on the Twelfth if it hadn't been for Brede getting hurt all these years ago. It was then I realised how pointless it all was. Now Kevin is more important to me than religion although it's all around us, but if it means we have to leave Belfast . . . well I would go.'

B 'When my sister, Brede, was hit on the head by a brick, I began to realise the troubles more times than not ended up hurting the innocent. So since then I've lost interest in 'hating' Protestants because I never knew why I hated them in the first place. And as far as a united Ireland is concerned, I don't know if it would be better for Catholics or not. I suppose the Prods would say they were being oppressed and the troubles would start all over again. I guess it's a no-win situation.'

C 'Sometimes I feel ashamed of being Catholic because of all the violence. I know it's on both sides but it's all so senseless it never gets us anywhere. People should realise what they're doing to each other. We're all human, aren't we? We're all the same . . . me, Tommy, Sadie, Kevin and Brian, Mum and Dad. I still believe in God but sometimes I wonder why He lets it happen and why He lets the killing go on. Why can't we live in peace? Why all the hate? You can't hate anyone any more when you're dead.'

D 'The way I see things is, I don't want to upset anyone. I love my Mum and Dad and I know Dad only gets upset because he loves us too. I am a Protestant. I've been brought up a Protestant. Kevin and Brede are nice and they are Catholic and now I realise there is good and bad in everything: good Catholics, bad Protestants; good Protestants, and bad Catholics. I wish Ireland didn't have its religions hating each other . . . Some way to believe in God! I don't ever want to go marching again because the music stirs my blood and before I know it I'll be thinking of Catholics as bogey-men again. My one true wish for Ireland is that people stop taking each others' blood, that we can live together in peace.'

E 'I live with my family on the Falls Road in Belfast. We are part of a very close-knit Roman Catholic community . . . we have to be close-knit because we are constantly struggling to preserve our identity in the face of British Government oppression. I believe that the only future this island has is a united one and, to achieve that, we Catholics must stick together and fight with all the means at our hands. We *must* not allow ourselves to be brainwashed by the British. We *will* not allow ourselves to be betrayed by our own kind . . .'

Talk

1 From what you have read in the play what other 'views' would you add to these?

2 What do you think other characters in the play believe? Mr Jackson? Mrs Jackson? Uncle Albert? Mr Mullet? Mrs Mullet? Mr Blake?

3 Which character do you think has the strongest religious beliefs? Explain your choice.

4 Which characters do you think are the most open-minded?

Write

Choose three characters.

• Re-read the scenes in which they appear.

• Make a list of any opinions they appear to show.

• Make a list of any important activities in which they are involved.

• In pairs, imagine you are one of your characters. Get your partner to ask you questions about your views and answer them in the role of your character.

• Write out their 'views' in a similar way to the ones you have just read.

Barricades to Love

Sadie   I'm not going out with Kevin because he's a Catholic, or a Mick or whatever you want to call him . . . I'm going out with him because he's Kevin . . . We like being with each other, we don't want to be with anyone else.

Read   Life in Northern Ireland is very difficult for couples from different religions, especially if they are married. Look at the article on the opposite page.

Talk
1   Look up the meaning of any words you do not understand in this article. What do you think the headline means?

2   What are your own family's beliefs? Do your parents or guardian follow a particular religion? Do you share their beliefs?

3   What would Sadie's and Kevin's parents have said to them if they had tried to get married? In pairs, imagine you are in one of the two households. Have the sort of conversation about mixed marriage that you think they would have had.

4   What advice would you give to a 'mixed' couple planning to marry and live in Northern Ireland? Think about their relationships with family, where they might live, what kind of school any children might go to.

Mixed Marriage - Running the Gauntlet of Disapproval

In the wake of the recent loyalist gun attack on the Caulfields, MARTIN O'HAGAN talks to couples involved in mixed marriages. And he writes that mixed couples are more readily accepted in Catholic areas but not by the Church.

"THEY SHOOT mixed marriages don't they", Martha said nervously. The Protestant wife of a Craigavon Catholic had just heard the early morning news that loyalist gunmen had murdered Margaret Caulfield, also a Protestant, and seriously wounded her Catholic husband Gerald as the couple lay sleeping in their North Belfast home.

Martha's reaction is indicative of the many people who have married outside their religion and who have run the gauntlet of disapproval from one side or the other. "I felt", she said of the Caulfields, "we had something in common even though we will never meet and now I feel the loss."

The Caulfields had only been married for three weeks at the time of the attack and despite their respective religions, there isn't any suggestion that the couple were practising Christians. They did not appear to be involved politically either. Their only crime was being involved in a 'mixed' marriage and living in a Protestant area.

Strictly speaking mixed marriages are those between a Christian and a non-Christian but in Northern Ireland it means a marriage between a Catholic and a Protestant.

A mixed marriage is often viewed as a betrayal of each other's faith and community and is often actively discouraged by both sides.

Jim, who married a Catholic from the Ormeau Road in Belfast had a "quiet wedding" because neither set of parents wanted the couple to get married. Since they weren't practising Christians, the couple felt that a wedding in a Registry Office would solve the problems posed by a church wedding especially if it had been a Catholic ceremony. Nevertheless, their only child goes to the local Catholic school because both now live in a Catholic area. Jim feels safer in the area where he thinks there is more tolerance. "But in their own way," he says, "people never let me forget I am an outsider."

Elizabeth, who lives in Portadown's frontline estate of Ballyoran was a Protestant but became a Catholic when she married. She says Protestants are "losing out" because they reject Catholicism and their Irishness. But even after 20 years, Elizabeth says she sometimes still feels like an outsider. She says she stopped children fighting in the street a few months ago and one of them turned and called her "an Orange bastard." "They could only have learned that from older people," she says.

Jill, whose baby is over a year old, never had the child baptised because the father, a Catholic, refused to give an undertaking that the child would be reared as a Catholic. Jill's husband believes this is moral blackmail and that strangers "in dog collars have no right to interfere in the running of my family. It's not them who puts bread on our table."

Many mixed couples send their children to integrated and independent schools such as Lagan and Forge. The Catholic Church has steadfastly refused to appoint a chaplain to these schools unlike its Protestant counterpart.

Families who would otherwise have no contact with one another are brought together through a mixed marriage. But after a marriage does little to break the divide. Elizabeth has brothers and sisters living in Protestant areas of Portadown but because of the town's sectarian divisions, they rarely meet. Some of Martha's Protestant relatives will talk to her when they meet on the street but there are others who ignore her.

When Martha's Catholic husband attended the funeral of his father-in-law several years ago, he said he felt unwelcome. He said he was ignored by most of Martha's family and "treated like a leper."

Read

In **Across the Barricades** we follow the relationship between Sadie Jackson who is a Protestant and Kevin McCoy who is a Catholic. This imaginary newspaper article was produced for a competition by a school student when the play was first produced. It tries to look at some of the difficulties which led them to leave Ireland.

FORBIDDEN LOVE

BELFAST COUPLE FORCED TO LEAVE HOME AND FAMILY BEHIND BECAUSE OF TERRORIST ATTACKS

by Teresa Wilmot

Kevin and Sadie are just like any other young couple in love. All they want is to be together and be happy. However, in Belfast that's too much to ask if one of you happens to be Catholic and the other Protestant. We talked to the young couple about what forced them to leave. Sadie Jackson, an attractive blonde, replied; "It was getting too much for me and Kevin, with me being a Protestant and him a Catholic. Our friends were all against us, and trying to split us up. My father even had a go with him because he is in the Orange Lodge and he is against Catholics. Because of me, Kevin was beaten up by terrorists. He could have died, he was in a terrible state."

Did you ever think it might have been better if you stopped seeing each other? The 17 year old Belfast teenager said: "Oh. Yes – when Kevin got attacked. His sister, Brede, came to me to ask me to stop seeing Kevin because it was getting too dangerous and that really put pressure on things. But I decided that I loved him and we couldn't bear to stop seeing each other."

We asked Kevin McCoy, 18: Do you think that there should be separate schools for Protestants and Catholics? He answered: "When I was younger, I would

have said 'yes'. But now that I have met Sadie, it's a different matter. I began to change my mind when she and Tommy (Sadie's brother) came to the hospital when Brede was unconscious and fighting for her life, after our battle with the Protestants. They were really nice. I realised that they were just the same as us."

We asked the young couple; Do you ever think you might go back to Belfast and see your family?

"No, I don't, not after the way they treated me and Kevin. I'll never go back," Sadie said in a determined voice.

We asked, "Won't you miss your family? I mean, You've lived with them all your life and to just get up and go like that . . ."

Sadie answered: "I can't tell a lie. I will miss them, but because of the way they behaved towards me and Kevin, I will never forgive them. Now I can understand the way they feel, probably because I feel something the same. We're scared and don't know where to go. We've got a bit of money, but that won't last for long. Once we get jobs though I don't think it will be too bad," Sadie said with an optimistic grin.

. . . .

Talk

1   Where do you think Teresa Wilmot imagines that she is interviewing the couple?

2   How old were Kevin and Sadie in the play?

3   What do you think they were doing at the time of this interview? How long do you think they had been there?

4   Do you think there should be separate schools for people with different religions? Before you come to a final decision about this, think of as many reason as you can both for and against this idea.

. . . .

Write

Produce a local newspaper article of your own looking at Kevin and Sadie's relationship.

• Decide what are the key moments in the relationship and make a list of them.

• Choose an important moment in their relationship on which to focus in your article.

• Imagine you are writing a series of features on love between people of different religious beliefs.

• Include lines from the play as quotations in your article or make up lines that you think Sadie and Kevin might have said.

• Set out your work in newspaper columns. You could type it and include an appropriate photograph to illustrate it.

Drama Ideas

1   In Scene 7, Kevin and Sadie are picked up by Albert who stops to give them a lift home. Using a few old seats the actors playing these parts then pretend to be in a real car.

In groups of four, build a 'human' car of your own. You can use people in your group to be some of the parts of the car (eg the bonnet, the wipers, the gear stick). Mime a car journey in which

- your car breaks down

- your car is chased by another car

- your car ends up in an unusual place . . .

2   **Sadie's job**

Sadie

I'd been bored stiff working in the hat department, watching all these stupid women trying on some really awful hats . . .

Get together as many hats as you can. In pairs, imagine you are Sadie and a customer.

a   Try on the different hats with Sadie pretending to be reasonably polite and the customer reacting to his or her own chosen hat.

b   Imagine Sadie is so bored that she can no longer be even moderately well-behaved. She starts trying on hats at the same time as the customers and putting on the voices that she thinks fit the hat she is wearing.

3   **Prejudice**

Many of the characters in **Across the Barricades** have prejudices, especially about religion.

In groups act some of these possible situations involving characters in the play.

- Sadie and Kevin are sitting having coffee in the kitchen in the Jackson household. Mr Jackson returns from the Lodge to find them there. Continue the scene.

- Kevin and Sadie are sitting drinking cans of coke in the garden of the McCoy household. Mr and Mrs McCoy are meant to be out shopping. They return home unexpectedly because Brian Rafferty has told them about Kevin and Sadie. Continue the scene.

- Brede and Tommy have found out about Kevin and Sadie's boat tickets.

Either they try and persuade them to stay in Ireland.
Or they surprise them at the docks to say goodbye.
Try out the scene.

4   Radio News Broadcast

There are a number of radio news flashes in **Across the Barricades.** In pairs, re-read some of these. Choose a moment in the play which you think would be suitable for a news item. Prepare your news item and record it on tape.

5   Key moments

We see several important moments for characters in this play, for example, Mr Blake's decision to allow Kevin and Sadie to meet in his house.

- Choose three characters from the play.

- Choose some moments you feel to be important to these characters.

- Put yourself in the shoes of one of the characters. In pairs, have your partner ask you questions about how you feel, why you behaved as you did, what your plans are, etc.

- When you feel you have got inside your character, make some notes about 'your' thoughts and feelings.

Write them up in the form of a day's diary extract.

Do the same for the other two characters.

6   Holiday in Belfast

Kevin

Belfast is a really beautiful city. We have got all these parks ... we've got the Botanic Gardens ... we even have a rose festival every July.

We tend only to hear about the bad news from Belfast, but, as Kevin points out, life for many people goes on as normal in a beautiful city.

Find out from a Travel Agents, from geography books, an encyclopaedia or any other sources what you can about Belfast.
In groups, prepare a radio or TV advertisement to sell a holiday in or near Belfast. If possible, record your advertisement on video or audio tape.

7   Drama from the news

Collect a number of your local newspapers. Cut out two or three articles that you think have some interesting stories behind them.

- Work out the characters you are going to include.

- Produce a short scene based on your local news and act it out.

8   Two Years On

What do you think happened to Kevin and Sadie?

Make up a scene showing them in two years' time from the end of the play. Write it out.

What the Author Says

When I wrote the first book about Catholic Kevin and Protestant Sadie growing up in Belfast – *The Twelfth Day of July,* which precedes *Across the Barricades* – my aim was to make it as balanced as possible. I did not want to be on one side or the other. I wanted to be *for* the Protestants and *for* the Catholics, seeing the good and the bad points in both. I wanted to write a book that would make my readers think about prejudice and the way we tend to divide up society into 'us' and 'them'.

In order to create a balance I decided to alternate chapters, moving between the Protestant and Catholic communities, so that they would occupy similar space in the book. I then balanced my characters by giving Kevin a sister, Brede, the same age as Sadie, and Sadie a brother, Tommy, the same age as Kevin. The action I set in the few days leading up to the Twelfth of July, the day when the Protestants celebrate the victory of King William of Orange (otherwise known as King Billy) over the Catholics at the Battle of the Boyne. That took place in 1690. Memories are long in Ireland.

At the start of *The Twelfth Day of July* Kevin and Sadie are outright enemies; by the end of it they have come to have some respect for one another and there is the beginning of an attraction between them. They have also come to challenge some of the prejudices and fears of their upbringing. I had no thoughts of writing a sequel but when I was working on the last chapter I realised that I had on my hands two characters who were going to refuse to lie down. I had to find out what happened to them next! So I went on to write *Across the Barricades*, and subsequently *Into Exile, A Proper Place* and *Hostages to Fortune*. Thus their story became a quintet and spanned seven – very important and crucial – years of their lives.

Joan Lingard

Joan Lingard described the book she wrote before **Across the Barricades – The Twelfth Day of July** – to help us understand what she was trying to do with Kevin and Sadie.

Talk

1   Do you think that the play of **Across the Barricades** gives a balanced view of Protestants and Catholics?

2   Did you want to find out what happened next to Kevin and Sadie? Explain you answer.

Write

Read one of the other three books in Joan Lingard's quintet. Choose a part of the book that you particularly enjoyed.

Try and produce your own adaptation of it in the form of one or two scenes for a play. Act out your version.

Across the Barricades on Stage

Across the Barricades was written to be performed in schools, without stage lighting, in a fast moving style.

Think

Imagine you are directing the play. How would you tackle these effects?

- the VOICE-OVER at the start of the play
- the NEWS BULLETINS
- the DREAM SEQUENCE (Scene 3)
- SOUND EFFECTS (for example the fight in Scene 3)

Read

David Ian Neville says in the opening stage directions that the set should look a bit like a junk yard. He suggests that scenes can be shown by using a few simple props, for example a few chairs and an old steering-wheel for Uncle Albert's car.

Task

Choose three scenes from the play. For each one decide which objects you would want to have on stage to suggest the place where the scene takes place. Draw a diagram to show how you would lay out the stage.

Music

In the play, Kevin and Sadie remember their love affair. At several key moments in the play the stage directions indicate that music is needed. Choose some music for at least two of these moments. Act out part or all of the scene with your music.

Design

Either design a poster to advertise a production of **Across the Barricades**.

Or make a programme to go with a production of the play. Include notes about the situation in Belfast, about the characters and about what you are trying to do in your production.

Act

In your class choose one section of the play which you would all enjoy acting out.

Divide your class into groups with the right number of actors and one extra person to be the director. (You may decide that one person can play more than one part.)

Before you act it out,

- decide how you are going to play your character

- if you are playing a part, work out the voice you are going to use, the mood you are in, what sort of person you are

- if you are the director, give advice to all of your actors about how they might play their parts, and listen to their own views ... suggest where they should move ... what they should do ...

- perform your different versions of the same section of this play

- talk about each version and how they compare ... try and make comments about the different ways each group chose to portray the characters and how they came over to you as the audience.

Reasons for conflict, and population charts, p. 8, from
Conflict in Northern Ireland by Tony McAleavy
(Holmes McDougall 1987), reproduced by permission
of Collins Educational.

Character profiles, p. 82–3, from Tag Theatre
Company's educational pack for *Across the Barricades*.

*Mixed Marriage – Running the Gauntlet of
Disapproval*, p. 85, by Martin O'Hagan, from *Fortnight*
magazine, June 1986.

Forbidden Love, p. 86, by Teresa Wilmot, from
Glasgow Herald/Tag Theatre Company Writing
Competition 1986.

Across the Barricades

The publishers would like to thank the following for
permission to reproduce photographs:

Camera Press p. 75 (top); Magnum/Ian Berry
p. 2,/Philip Jones Griffiths p. 79,/Gilles Peress pp. 51
(left), 70, 89,/Chris Steele-Perkins pp. 7, 22, 31;
Northern Ireland Tourist Board pp. 51 (right), 91;
Popperfoto p. 75 (bottom).

Illustrations are by Peter Melnyczuk.

Plays in this series include:

Across the Barricades   ISBN 0 19 831272 5
   Joan Lingard   adapted by David Ian Neville

The Burston School Strike   ISBN 0 19 831274 1
   Roy Nevitt

The Demon Headmaster   ISBN 0 19 831270 9
   Gillian Cross   adapted by Adrian Flynn

Frankenstein   ISBN 0 19 831267 9
   Mary Shelley   adapted by Philip Pullman

Hot Cakes   ISBN 0 19 831273 3
   Adrian Flynn

Paper Tigers   ISBN 0 19 831268 7
   Steve Barlow and Steve Skidmore

A Question of Courage   ISBN 0 19 831271 7
   Marjorie Darke   adapted by Bill Lucas and Brian Keaney

The Teen Commandments   ISBN 0 19 831275 X
   Kelvin Reynolds

Tigers on the Prowl   ISBN 0 19 831277 6
   Steve Barlow and Steve Skidmore

The Turbulent Term of Tyke Tiler   ISBN 0 19 831269 5
   adapted from her own novel by Gene Kemp